The Health

The Health of the Nation

NHS in Peril

David Owen

Methuen

Published by Methuen & Co

Methuen & Co
35 Hospital Fields Road
York YO10 4DZ

www.methuen.co.uk

First published 2014

1

Typeset by SX Composing DTP, Rayleigh, Essex
Printed by CPI Group (UK) Ltd, Croydon, CR0 4YY

ISBN: 978-0-413-77772-0
Ebook ISBN: 978-0-413-77773-7

A CIP catalogue record for this book is
available from the British Library

To Tessa, Sylvan, Cai and Elizabeth, in the hope and expectation that the NHS will serve them as well as it has served my generation since 1948

Contents

Acknowledgements

I have been fortunate to be able to draw extensively from two published reports: firstly Nicholas Timmins, *Never Again? The Story of the Health and Social Care Act 2012 – A Study in Coalition Government and Policy Making* (Institute for Government, 2012), and secondly Olivia O'Sullivan and Elizabeth Woodcraft (eds), *Report of the Lewisham People's Commission*, available online at www.savelewishamhospital.com/peoples-commission-report. I have also taken a long quote about the People's March from Jarrow in the summer of 2014 from the Staggers blog. I have deliberately used on many occasions fairly long quotes from speeches, articles and letters of other people because I wanted to convey a sense that the reinstatement of the NHS is a people's demand.

Many people have helped me, too numerous to mention, since I first began as a medical student in 1956 and as an MP in 1966; to all of them I owe a huge debt. This book, however, could never have been completed without the support of Peter Tummons at my publisher Methuen, Jonathan Wadman, my editor, and Maggie Smart, who has worked with me since 1977. To them I owe a special debt of gratitude.

Introduction

The major consequence of the 2012 Health and Social Care Act has been how it views health care in England as a business rather than a service. The key political challenge today for many people in England is how to persuade politicians that they are wrong to believe that health should be viewed in this way, and to explain how we can sensibly reinstate the fundamentals of the NHS that are being dismantled in England, fundamentals that elsewhere in the United Kingdom remain intact and widely supported, as we saw during the Scottish referendum.

Along with Scotland, Wales and Northern Ireland have retained an undoubtedly recognisable NHS, albeit in slightly different forms. Only in England does the threat exist that the NHS will be unrecognisable by 2020 if the 2012 legislation is not repealed in substance after the May 2015 general election. But this has profound implications for the UK.

The underlying reasons that make the original concept of the NHS worth fighting for are clear, but not often stated, perhaps because they go to the ethical and moral basis of the way many UK citizens wish to live their lives. There is a natural reserve which makes many people reluctant to talk about these values in a political setting. But at the next election we must drop that reserve and fight not just an ideological battle but a struggle for the heart. Politics is not solely about power; it is also about people and how to make power serve the people.

In 1952 the founder of the NHS wrote these words, which sum up the timeless moral case for the reinstatement of a recognisable NHS in England: 'Society becomes more wholesome, more serene and spiritually healthier if it knows that its citizens have at the back of their consciousness the knowledge that not only themselves but also their fellows have access when ill, to the best that medical skill can provide.'[1] 'Wholesome' is a wonderful word and so is 'serene'. To live without the fear of being unable to afford medical care is a blessing, but one which has only been with us since 1948 in the UK. The market does not have to penetrate every nook and cranny of our day-to-day life.

In the nineteenth century the philosopher Thomas Carlyle warned of the marketisation that was starting to feed through into all parts of society:

> We have profoundly forgotten everywhere that cash-payment is not the sole relation of human beings; we think nothing of doubting, that it absolves and liquidates all engagements of man. 'My starving workers?' answers the rich mill-owner. 'Did I not hire them fairly in the market?

---

1 Aneurin Bevan, *In Place of Fear* (Heinemann, 1952).

Did I not pay them, to the last sixpence, the sum covenanted for? What have I to do with them more? [2]

The social history of the NHS makes clear that it would be 'an error to regard the NHS as a spontaneous creation'. The cumbersome National Health Insurance (NHI) administration established in 1911 supplied minimum financial relief during sickness and a 'panel doctor' service for the low paid on the basis of weekly deductions of income for the so-called health stamp.[3] But many were not covered by this insurance. There was nothing for those excluded other than the charity of the doctor or a hospital. The Dawson report of 1920 pointed the way but many slum dwellers had totally inadequate healthcare, if any, and lived in conditions of Dickensian squalor. The Second World War brought the Emergency Medical Service, the Beveridge report and the 1944 White Paper outlining the provisions of the projected NHS: a resolve emerged in wartime within the British people that when peace came there would be a different and better system of healthcare for everyone.

In 2014, the political writer David Marquand wrote about the profound dangers to the NHS of what amounts 'to a transition from a managed market to an unmanaged one'.[4] What is more complicated about this market and more important 'has to do with the mentality and rhetoric of the marketisers and with the social vision they encapsulate'. At the heart of all marketisation and commercialisation of the NHS lies the 'totemic term

---

2 Thomas Carlyle, *Past and Present* (Chapman & Hall, 1843).

3 Charles Webster, *The National Health Service: A Political History* (Oxford University Press, 1998).

4 David Marquand, *Mammon's Kingdom: An Essay on Britain, Now* (Allen Lane, 2014).

"choice": free choice by unconnected individuals, satisfying individual wants through market competition'.

Healthcare, whether public or private, in a very real sense is infinite: money can be – and in many countries is – poured into healthcare by those who can afford it. Money for the NHS is a public choice, but it is all relative to what we choose to spend on education, housing, welfare, defence, all legitimate demands. Healthcare, if publicly provided, inevitably has to be constrained. That rationing process within the NHS is flexible, professional and democratically accountable. It is decided by Parliament through the Chancellor of the Exchequer, the Secretary of State for Health and Cabinet. By democratic choice it is not done by a market or by insurance premiums. Voters could have chosen a different system – they exist in many parts of the world – but no major political party has ever felt brave or foolish enough to put that choice to them. It was not, as this book will show, a choice put to the electorate in 2010 by either the Conservatives or Liberal Democrats.

The unknowing nature of choice when applied to healthcare dramatically demonstrates the problem that many politicians and journalists have when they come to make quick appreciations, half-decisions and slick prescriptions for the NHS. The reality is that healthcare is a constant learning curve. There are few certainties. Roger Taylor, a journalist who works on the annual *Dr Foster Hospital Guide*, explains: 'For much of the healthcare we deliver, we really don't know whether it is safe or effective.'[5] He identifies an 'astonishing

---

5 Roger Taylor, *God Bless the NHS: The Truth behind the Current Crisis* (Faber & Faber, 2013).

divide' between the politicians and the people, writing that for

> the past 20 years the corridors of the Department of Health have thronged with people who believe that greater private provision is what the NHS needs, yet if one steps outside and starts to poll the public, one struggles to find people who express any degree of enthusiasm for that idea.

We cannot even be certain that what doctors think patients want is what they actually want. Doctors asked in a survey to rate the top priorities for patients undergoing chemotherapy reckoned that extending life was the priority for 96 per cent of patients. Yet when the patients were asked, only 59 per cent agreed. As a statistician Professor Sir Brian Jarman, a practising GP, as well as an epidemiologist, kept a tally of the frequency with which the word 'hindsight' was used in the public inquiry on the Mid-Staffordshire Hospital Trust and he calculated by the end of 139 days of hearings that it had been used 456 times. Everywhere one looks in surveys and statistics covering healthcare one finds questions raised which are not answered and divisions revealed which are not resolved. This unknowing is in the very nature of medical care; certainty is rare.

Yet how does one explain the amazing popularity of the NHS, even after much-publicised scandals, like Mid-Staffordshire Hospital? People know only too well that the demand for ever more expensive healthcare cannot be met. They understand that there have to be financial disciplines; they recognise, without necessarily using the word, that the NHS is a democratically rationed healthcare system. They like the NHS, despite at times its many shortcomings, because they sense that its care choices are broadly fair and they prize its comprehensive cover. Most families have deep-seated memories where they do literally bless the NHS. They can complain, they can get angry and they are demanding, rightly, to be better able to influence that rationing process. But the general public fear that once the health service becomes driven by market principles, the rationing will cease to be fair and their care will become driven by profits. They see that drive for profit every day in the supermarkets, in their gas and electricity and water bills. They know the difference between a true competitive market and an imperfect market: cost savings stem from the former while high costs reflect the latter. They reject a market for their overall healthcare. They may have insurance to cover some private care but the vast majority use the family doctor service. People sense that medical advice dominated by profit-based private interests will not always be in their best interests. They are right in their apprehensions. Experience around the world demonstrates that there is real value in both senses of the word in publicly provided comprehensive healthcare cover available for every citizen.

The campaign for the reinstatement of our NHS draws on these principles but in the context of the second decade of the twenty-first century and within the ethos of the social market now enshrined within the treaties of a European Union comprising twenty-eight very different and distinct states. Most people accept that we cannot abolish all charging or market elements or private contractors in such a large concern as the NHS. They have existed since 1948. People do believe, however, that an organisation that carries the brand name NHS has to practice under a fair trade description, and that means that the preferred provider should be the NHS.

The Campaign for the NHS Reinstatement Bill 2015 is an all-party and no-party campaign[6] whose aim is simple: to ensure a sufficient number of MPs are returned to Parliament in May 2015 so that whichever party or combination of parties form the government the marketisation of healthcare is removed from the Health and Social Care Act 2012 – which in essence only applies to England. This Act was likened when it was published to tossing a hand grenade into the NHS. The damage it has done already is hard to exaggerate, let alone quantify. This legislation must be repealed but it will have to be done carefully in an enabling way, with no single appointed day when everything changes.

We must not forget in the context of the NHS that in September 2014 the Scottish independence referendum brought the United Kingdom perilously close to splitting apart. Those elements that we share, that help create a sense of common purpose, should become ever more precious as we try to unify our nation. Politics cannot be an ideology-free zone but it should not resound with zealotry. We saw in that Scottish referendum how powerful a vote swinger the NHS became in the closing stages of the campaign. Despite the fact that health is fully devolved to the Scottish Parliament, the spectre of an English-controlled Treasury being able to use financial allocations to bring marketisation to Scotland's NHS carried sufficient weight with voters that the 'yes' campaign exploited it and the 'no' campaign feared it. It also served to remind some voters, not just in Scotland, that the NHS as we have known it since 1948

---

6 www.nhsbill2015.org

was under threat, whereas in Scotland, Northern Ireland and Wales it is continuing.

In the context of more financial devolution to Scotland, the post-referendum mood in England is for recognition that on devolved matters like health English MPs need a more powerful proportional voice within a single Westminster Parliament serving the UK as a whole. The answer to that natural demand and what has become popularly identified as the 'West Lothian question' was addressed by a commission chaired by Sir William McKay, Clerk to the House of Commons from 1998 until 2002.[7] Three other commissioners came from universities in Belfast, Edinburgh and Aberystwyth and the fifth commissioner had been first parliamentary counsel in the Cabinet Office from 2006 to 2012.

As always, constitutional change should be evolutionary and never more so than for that complex and flexible instrument of our democracy, the House of Commons. It must also, even in the shadow of the referendum in Scotland, go with the grain of English nature. I detect no wish for a separate English parliament, nor for regional government. This is why the McKay commission is so timely in its recommendations. The five commissioners have found a solution with the delicacy of watchmakers, crafted with the skill of seasoned and acute observers of Parliament.

Theirs is an ingenious and groundbreaking reform. They propose that using a grand committee system, 'decisions at the United Kingdom level with a separate and distinct effect for

---

7 *Report of the Commission on the Consequences of Devolution for the House of Commons,* March 2013.

England (or for England and Wales) should normally be taken only with the consent of a majority of MPs for constituencies in England (or England and Wales)' (para. 119), while ensuring that 'the right of the House of Commons as a whole to make the final decision should remain' (para. 14). They have carved out a mechanism allowing that some English legislation would not have to be part of the normal procedure on all occasions. The commissioners assert: 'We would expect departures from the norm to occur only rarely in practice' (para. 142) and 'The apparent fragility of the declaratory resolution approach can also be seen as flexibility. A government, after consideration, may decide that it is necessary in the interests of the UK as a whole, or an affected part of it, to invoke the exception implicit in the word "normally"' (paras 173–4).

The report preserves the present position in the House of Commons that there should not be two different kinds of MPs, so all MPs would vote on whether to grant a second reading for all Bills and finally whether a Bill should become law with a single vote on third reading. If some English legislation has from time to time so great an implication for the UK as a whole that it does not fit with only English MPs amending it at committee and report stages, then Parliament can decide to make it UK legislation. The House of Commons should negotiate McKay's various options on an all-party basis. They will be able, I suspect, to get agreement on these purely House of Commons matters and the system could operate during the next parliament. The relevance of all this to the Campaign for the NHS Reinstatement Bill 2015 is that this Bill is a classic case of the sort of legislative exception that the McKay commissioners had in mind. It would be open to any political party to indicate in advance at the time of a general election its intention to exercise the exception for specific legislation.

The campaign exists to convince whoever forms the next government, either a single party on its own or any of the possible combinations, that there is a settled wish from the great bulk of voters for the original NHS to be available in all parts of the UK in a recognisable form. It would be a unifying theme for the next UK government to reinstate the NHS, at a time when the UK needs to revive a sense of unity.

There is another aspect to the Scottish referendum, the wish it has inspired for England to devolve more decisions to its bigger cities: London, Birmingham, Manchester, Leeds, Liverpool and Newcastle. In part this follows the success story of the gradual introduction of powerful mayors but there are cities such as Birmingham that are thriving on the traditional model of local government. There is a strong case for considering a strategic health and caring role for such cities. It would need to be introduced carefully on the basis of proven experience, not all happening at once, and would stem from a well-considered proposal from a city put to the Secretary of State for Health, who would have the enabling power to introduce it.

Constitutional change in a democracy usually is the result of a political trade-off and the changes that are pledged for Scotland will impact on Wales and Northern Ireland. In the next parliament there should be agreement on not just the McKay commission package but two other vital reforms which would reinforce the structure of UK unity: first, a smaller House of Commons and second, an elected Senate representing the four elements of the UK. The House of Lords has become an absurdity in size and composition. It reeks of patronage.

The time for an elected four-nation second chamber, revising laws across the UK, has now come. If there were to be some appointed members they could vote on non-legislative matters, while speaking on any subject, but only elected members should vote on legislation. For example, the voices of experts on health issues could add wisdom to debate and in select committees they could be full participants. But actual legislation would follow the democratic method and that could only be passed by elected members. This proposition was a compromise discussed in 1911, the last time the Lords was seriously reformed. Lords reform for some is an old chestnut better left well alone, but it is exploding under the load of its own contradictions. Reform offers a path to enlightened federalism.

The soul of our British healthcare system is well described in a book titled *NHS SOS*.[8] Many voters are simply not prepared to see it destroyed. Churchill, Eden, Macmillan, Douglas-Home and Major did not want to dismantle it, and Thatcher deemed it too 'politically toxic' to do so, but Cameron and Clegg, neither of whose parties won the election of 2010 and with no democratic mandate whatsoever, have started the process. The chapter in that book titled 'A Failure of Politics' makes heart-rending reading for Liberal Democrats. A party activist describes how successive policy conferences were manipulated so as to stop real debate, a particularly bitter pill for Liberals to swallow. For many Labour supporters there are descriptions of the Blair government's ill-conceived reforms, including accepting a revision of GP contracts to work only office hours, which paved

---

8 Jacky Davis and Raymond Tallis (eds), *NHS SOS: How the NHS Was Betrayed – and How We Can Save It* (Oneworld, 2013).

the way by legislation in 2006 for some of the market changes in the Health and Social Care Act 2012. In Chapter 2, 'Ready for Market', there is a very disturbing analysis of why GP contracts were changed. The scale of the opt-out from out-of-hours provision is alleged to be what the government fully anticipated and wanted. 'Out-of-hours provision also proved to be a useful entry point into primary care for private companies, an opening soon exploited . . . by such companies as Serco and Harmoni.' For members of the BMA and for members and fellows of the royal colleges, the inadequacies of those organisations are forensically dissected. Chapter 4, 'The Silence of the Lambs', also provides details of the shameful failure of the BBC to highlight what was going on. The actual reporting of the NHS from 2002 is researched in great detail in Chapter 6 'Hidden in Plain Sight', and it makes uncomfortable reading.

We all have our stories of what is wrong with parts of the NHS; nothing is perfect and to pretend all is going well in the NHS is absurd. But it is from the absurd and the ridiculous that you can detect underlying flaws. Relatively recently a member of my family developed a post-operative abscess and I accompanied them shortly after midnight to one of the most modern hospitals, recently built under a private finance initiative (PFI). The young doctor and nurses in the A&E unit were excellent, but there was no bed available. However, without demur the night was spent in Casualty. Next morning happened to coincide with a routine outpatient clinic of the consultant surgeon, which we both attended. The surgeon wanted immediate admission to operate under a general anaesthetic to drain the abscess. The bed manager refused admission. Eventually it was arranged that we would go out via the front door and turn right into A&E. Admission took place quickly since the notes had been transferred over; the bed manager's block was circumvented. An absurd and ridiculous performance. The abscess turned out to be an MRSA infection from the original elective surgery, only going to show that probably the biggest single category of illness remains iatrogenic, that caused by doctors intervention which is why the case for intervention has to be weighed carefully.

The aim of this book is to draw attention to the potential for the individual to exercise their democratic rights in ways that would have been impossible before the internet and the whole new era of electronic communications. These technologies have opened up the old style of campaigning to new means of persuasion. But to be effective they require a strong personal commitment, not in terms of money but in terms of time: time taken to absorb and understand the complexities of the NHS; time taken to communicate with MPs and parliamentary candidates; and persistence not to let candidates escape behind generalised party political manifestos and bland public relations statements devised on the back of focus groups. The new tools of communication are potentially very powerful but as yet their use is in its infancy. They are the new democratic way of exercising the power of the people.

In order to save the soul of the NHS, it is very clear that the lead must come from the people. People who, irrespective of which political party they support, are persuaded that on this issue of restoring the NHS they will not accept the 2012 legislation remaining on the statute book. People determined to improve the quality of healthcare, determined to champion a fundamental cultural change within the NHS to pursue greater efficiency without an external market and the commercialisation inherent in such an approach, and determined to seek ways to increase informed patient choice.

A one-nation UK should want the health systems within it to be similar but not necessarily the same. If the differences between them become too great, we run the grave risk of reaching a point identifiable by future social historians as the moment the UK started to break up. Ours is at this moment in our history a fragile Union. We all need to respect and value, whatever political parties we support, those elements which bind the citizens of the UK together. The referendum debate, whatever its logic, showed that emotionally a UK-wide NHS is one of those elements that can bind us together or split us apart. David Cameron needs to understand that to play the 'English card' on financial devolution in the way he did outside 10 Downing Street at 7 a.m. on the day after the Scottish referendum vote was a grave mistake which could yet have far-reaching constitutional consequences. The closest analogy I can find is when David Lloyd George on 5 December 1921 infamously threatened 'war within three days', if all the members of the Irish delegation did not sign the Anglo-Irish Treaty. It was, as it turned out, a very dangerous bluff. At 2.20 a.m. the treaty was signed but not by all. Lord Birkenhead in the British government delegation commented, 'I may have signed my political death warrant,' to which Michael Collins, leading the Irish delegation, perceptively replied, 'I may have signed my actual death warrant.' Lloyd George's intervention when revealed to the Dáil damaged Collins and though the vote went through it was despite of not because of it. Collins was at that stage despite Éamon de Valera's opposition recognised as a man of not just physical but also moral courage.[9] Cameron should learn this lesson from history: holding the UK together is still a task that requires the long view.

It is no paradox that the break-up of a UK-wide NHS threatens the integrity of the UK. We need elements other than the most obvious one of the defence of the realm to bind the UK together. The aftermath of the referendum in Scotland has not lifted the threat of separation but given the UK a little more time to achieve the correct balance between its constituent parts. The NHS offers us an additional opportunity to recapture an important element. Healthcare goes to the heart of what it has meant to be British for sixty-six years. It was no accident that Danny Boyle used the NHS as a defining characteristic in the opening ceremony of the 2012 Olympics.

It is very obvious that the SNP envisages a key role in shaping the next Westminster Parliament. If they do well in the general election it does not necessarily mean no Labour government after 2015, as some assume. Alex Salmond, now no longer leader, is contemplating running for the Westminster Parliament again, where he sat from 1987 until 2010. The *Financial Times* reported on 14 November 2014:

He made it clear that the SNP would be unlikely to join a Labour-led formal coalition. 'The best positioning for parties in that situation [of a minority administration] is to negotiate point by point.' He noted that in the past the party had voted on non-Scottish bills such as the

---

9 See T. Ryle Dwyer, *Big Fellow, Long Fellow. A Joint Biography of Collins and De Valera* (Gill & Macmillan, 1998).

introduction of university tuition fees and foundation hospitals.

This mention of foundation hospitals is important to note. Salmond was in the House of Commons and watched the long-drawn-out fight in effect between Tony Blair and Gordon Brown on this very issue. On 19 November 2003, the House of Commons voted by 302 votes to 285, a margin of seventeen to the proposed introduction of foundation hospitals. The House of Lords then that evening voted to reject the proposal. But in the early hours of the next morning the government with a majority of 41 reinstated the measure. At various times eighty-seven Labour MPs voted against the proposals and if they had ever combined, the proposals, though backed by Blair, would have been lost since the Conservatives in opposition were voting against foundation hospitals, as were the Liberal Democrats and the SNP. The Health and Social Care (Community Health and Standards) Act received Royal Assent on 20 November 2003.

One official told Anthony Seldon, 'Usually we managed to iron out differences between the Treasury and Number 10 by Jeremy Heywood [now Cabinet Secretary] and Andrew Adonis [now a peer and Labour shadow Transport Minister] sitting down with Ed Miliband and Ed Balls but on foundation hospitals this usual channel broke down.'[10]

Eventually a compromise was hammered out by the then Cabinet Secretary, Andrew Turnbull, and Simon Stevens, then working for Blair and now the coalition government's controversial choice as chief executive for NHS England. Stevens

---

10 Anthony Seldon, *Blair Unbound* (Simon & Schuster, 2007), pp. 240–7.

drafted the minute of the decision with Turnbull looking over his shoulder. The 'top-performing' hospitals (now under the Conservatives meaning all trust hospitals) were to become independent 'public interest' companies for largely NHS patients, though not run or owned by the NHS. They would have the right to borrow money but the Treasury would have the right to decide how much money they could all borrow, which would be limited, and the justification for this was that if the foundation trusts borrowed too much and went bankrupt the taxpayer would still have to bail them out.

It is no wonder that Brown and Salmond to this day dislike the very concept of foundation hospitals, and with considerable rational evidence for their criticisms. Legislative changes need to be introduced after 2015 to empower the Secretary of State for Health to remove some of the foundations' independence, but in a non-disruptive way. It could also be highly relevant that Nicola Sturgeon, the new SNP leader and former Scottish Health Secretary, committed the SNP at their annual conference on 15 November 2014 to 'never, ever' – words rarely used by politicians – go into government with the Conservatives in a minority government. She also pledged to continue to give a real-terms increase in spending to the NHS in Scotland.

Anyone who believes the present coalition policies for the NHS are not going to be a major and deeply contentious issue in May 2015 is living in cloud-cuckoo land. The task of the Campaign for the NHS Reinstatement Bill 2015 is to present a credible legislative reform package and rally support for it among existing MPs and prospective candidates of all UK parties.

I asked a dedicated NHS physician and wise scientist when writing this book what in one word was wrong with the NHS in England in 2014. The answer was short and precise: 'morale'. I tried to tease out from him and others the meaning of that single word 'morale', the many aspects which in combination contributed to its lowering. Some of them were close to 'moral' in their origin. Here are a few.

- The relentless growth of agency staff from cleaners to nurses within hospitals so that they lost a sense of identification with the hospital. No longer did the cleaner know the patients, nor did the nurses on the ward know the patients, the cleaners or the porters. In the past they were part of the team, known by name, respected for their contribution by other staff and patients, and as a consequence they had pride in their work.

- The inflexibility of the management at every level, not least the emergence of the authoritative bed manager.

- The sense of restriction rather than liberation that came with foundation trust status: the tight boundaries between hospitals, the competition, the lack of cooperation, the feeling that each one was a castle.

- The joint hierarchy of decision-making, from the level of the Department of Health right down to the running of a daily or weekly clinic, had been lost whereby health professionals' input had been matched by a managers'. The problem now was not so much the increase in managers as the distance between their view of the future NHS and that of the professionals.

In the pick of the week's correspondence from many newspapers published by *The Week* on 9 March 2013, at the time of controversy over whether the chief executive of the NHS, Sir David Nicholson, should resign, one letter stood out:

> Your leader 'Hospital Pass' reaches the wrong conclusion that the NHS is now more efficient with the current financial arrangements. Indeed, it is precisely the business culture encouraged by the internal market and the split between providers and purchasers which is responsible for some of the unsatisfactory attitudes so widely reported.
>
> It has been clear to most working in the NHS that the so-called market has been inappropriate for healthcare since it was introduced in the 1990s. The idea of competition between health providers, plus the purchaser/provider split, are accepted by most politicians, journalists, health economists and yourselves as the only ways to motivate people in the NHS to work harder and improve efficiency.
>
> In fact it does the opposite. Services are valued only for the income they earn. This leads to the demoralisation and demotivation of staff, especially for those working in areas thought not to be good income generators. Kindness, compassion and dedication cannot be measured and, therefore, cannot be priced like a commodity. It is these qualities which we need to foster by returning to old standards of professionalism. A return to a planned healthcare system, as happens in Scotland, would promote an integrated approach to healthcare and would help to restore professionalism, pride and satisfaction in working in the NHS. It would also help to make the billions of savings now required by eliminating much of the hugely wasteful and complex commissioning process that consumes 14

per cent of total NHS costs. Whether or not Sir David Nicholson remains in post is irrelevant. He is only doing the will of his political masters who fail to understand that healthcare is not a business.

Professor Robert Elkeles
Consultant physician and professor of diabetic medicine
Northwood, Herts

Healthcare is not like any other business or utility like gas, water or electricity and I hope this will be very clear to everyone who reads this book. It is why on the cover of the book I have placed a photograph of a plaque on a public building which has the translation of a saying from Cicero: 'THE HEALTH OF THE PEOPLE IS THE HIGHEST LAW.' It is a mark of shame that in the twenty-first century British politicians, both Labour and Conservative, forgot this truth. Let the people who know better now teach their politicians an important lesson. We are not going to let you destroy the NHS in England, for in so doing you are risking the unity of the United Kingdom.

Action Sheet

To join the campaign to restore the NHS in England you should visit the campaign website at http://www.nhsbill2015.org.

All we ask is that during the months leading up to the general election you approach by letter, email, interview or questions at public meetings, your constituency parliamentary candidates, and anyone you know personally who might be standing in another constituency.

Please ask relatives and friends to do the same.

You should approach candidates irrespective of your own political beliefs.

You should aim to establish a dialogue about why you believe that fundamental changes are needed after the next election to the Health and Social Care Act 2012.

Please persist even if given the brush-off or formalised replies.

Cite instances of local opportunities or of failures in the NHS where the campaign's Reinstatement Bill would be beneficial.

This campaign is an extension of democracy and most candidates will not resent being asked but some might resist.

Register candidates' response, whether positive or negative, on our website.

It is best to adopt a personal, not a formal, approach and put questions in your own words on these two core issues:

1. 'Will you vote, if elected, for the NHS Reinstatement Bill?' The Bill is on the campaign website. You can summarise it, print it off or refer the candidate to the website.

2. 'If you are not ready to support this Bill, why not?' Democratic elections mean you have a right to question your candidates' intentions and to ask for detailed replies to specific questions. In the old days this was done at public meetings called hustings. They have gone out of fashion but where they are taking place we suggest you attend and record the answers given.

Be open and transparent at all times and do not be provocative. Let the candidates know that you will be sending their reply, or failure to reply, to the campaign website where they will be free to correct anything that purports to be their view.

Please return all this information to us with your name, your constituency, your address and wherever possible your suggestion for what would make a fair quote, being a specific and representative part of the candidate's own words or what you are interpreting as their position. This will then go on the campaign website. It will of course then be open to any candidate to correct or extend their views.

Before 7 May 2015 many MPs and candidates – Conservative, Labour, Liberal Democrat, UKIP, Green, SNP, Plaid Cymru – will be systematically challenged to indicate whether they will support the NHS Reinstatement Bill in England. In Scotland, Wales and Northern Ireland, urge candidates to commit to vote, if elected as an MP, for reinstatement of the NHS in England. Allow marketisation and commercialisation to continue in England and it will not be long before it affects the NHS throughout the United Kingdom. The NHS in one part of the UK means the NHS in all of the UK. They will never be exactly the same for they are part of devolved government but they are inextricably linked.

Chapter 1

The Hung Parliament of 2010

Politicians will long argue whether it was the actual arithmetic of the number of MPs elected which was the real determinant of the Liberal Democrats choosing to go into coalition with the Conservatives or whether the Liberal Democrats had become more like continental Liberal parties in advocating market solutions in ways more ideological than the Christian Democratic parties. They had also developed an antagonism to Labour that grew the longer Labour held office. Nick Clegg had given two criteria publicly which would guide him and his party as to which party they would negotiate with first. They would choose the party with the largest number of MPs in Parliament *and* with the largest number of votes. Since the Conservatives met both of these criteria they were in the dominant position from the start. Only a very clear commitment from Gordon Brown to give up being Labour's Prime Minister immediately a new government was formed on the Friday afternoon would have begun to shift that formula approach from the Liberal Democrats. But Labour's electoral college procedure for choosing a new leader posed a dilemma: it took far too long to be used in this case. They would have had to put forward a figure who would be unopposed by Labour MPs.

After David Cameron's speech on the Friday afternoon, all that was left for those Liberal Democrat MPs who were reluctant to join a Conservative coalition was to argue for simultaneous negotiations with Labour. These eventually did start but met with no great enthusiasm from the key Labour figures. Labour had done very little pre-planning and their most enthusiastic negotiator was Lord Adonis, but less influential for not being an elected MP. The battle was fought out in four action-packed days. Accounts of what went on from the viewpoints of the three main parties were subsequently published, the best being Adonis's.[11]

Staying on at No. 10 while negotiations to form a government took place was Brown's constitutional duty. It was very unfair to depict him as 'clinging to office', a claim his detractors tried to pin on him that Monday. But his offer to the Liberal Democrats involving a delay in giving up the role of Prime Minister until the autumn, during which time a new Labour leader would be elected, was by then clearly not negotiable. For the general public to have had any confidence in such a deal Labour had to have a new Prime Minister in place. But they failed to provide an emergency procedure for such an eventuality. The 'constitutional' expectation that the incumbent Prime Minister should never leave the country in a situation in which there is no government, nor the sovereign

---

11 Andrew Adonis, *5 Days in May: The Coalition and Beyond* (Biteback, 2013); David Laws, *22 Days in May: The Birth of the Lib Dem–Conservative Coalition* (Biteback, 2010); Rob Wilson, *5 Days to Power: The Journey to Coalition Britain* (Biteback, 2010).

without a clear choice of a new Prime Minister, needs more explaining to the public.

Nick Clegg, who wanted more time on the Monday to bargain a better deal, was also wanting to clinch the Conservative offer and he expected the Prime Minister to hang about into the late evening. Such a process would have involved Brown being depicted by the press as leaving Downing Street ('like a burglar' as Ed Balls put it) late that night. The Cabinet Secretary should have been empowered to make public announcements during this time about the proper procedures that needed to be completed. There was an inevitable drum beat from the press for an early decision, even though in other countries with more frequent coalitions the process is expected to take weeks and the previous government remains in office in a caretaker capacity. If we are to face another hung parliament in 2015, perhaps with three or more parties forming a government, whether in coalition or not, we should raise public expectations that the process is not instantaneous.

Personally I approached the arrival of the Conservative–Liberal Democrat coalition with an open mind. I stayed a crossbencher in the House of Lords, never having joined the Liberal Democrats. It seemed that the coalition was what the country wanted. Not only had people voted so as to make its creation most likely, but in a strange way that our 'first-past-the-post' voting system can sometimes produce, by and large most people thought, given the parliamentary arithmetic, it was what the country should have.

In as much as the NHS was a specific issue it seemed that there was little enthusiasm in Gordon Brown's Labour Party for a market in healthcare, nor did Nick Clegg's continental

Liberal enthusiasm for the market economy extend to health. David Cameron having specifically and frequently committed himself to no more top-down reorganisations of the health service, the pace of any change was likely to be slow: no faster than what had gone on before. Cameron was keen to demonstrate his commitment to the NHS emotionally as well as in theory before and during the election. In an unintrusive way he reminded people how much his own family owed to the NHS when his eldest son, who had sadly died, was under treatment within it.

A story of what then happened, against all predictions, to create the Health and Social Care Act 2012 was commissioned by two independent bodies: the well-regarded new Institute for Government and the older King's Fund. I have drawn below extensively on their account because it simply would not be believed unless it had come from such an independent source. David Cameron, who once was happy to see himself labelled as the 'heir to Blair', must as Prime Minister take the main responsibility for the government's hoodwinking of the people. Also incompetent implementation of the legislation, earning in full *The Times* headline 'NHS reforms our worst mistake, Tories admit'.[12]

The author, Nicholas Timmins, entitled the research 'Never Again'. He had been public policy editor of the *Financial Times* and is currently a visiting professor in social policy at the LSE and in public management at King's College London. In the prologue of what he calls 'something of a political thriller' he writes that it is a story that can be easily told:

---

12 *The Times*, 13 October 2014.

A man in a hurry who was part of a coalition government (that just weeks earlier had promised the country 'no more top-down reorganisations' of the National Health Service) launched arguably the biggest restructuring it had seen in its 63-year history. He did so without having told anyone what he was up to – at least as far as most of the public and the staff of the NHS were concerned.

So great was the resistance – not least from the grass roots of one part of the coalition – that the Government was forced into an unprecedented 'pause' over its legislation. The pause, however, failed to silence the critics. There were times when it looked like the bill would be lost. In fact it got through. It did so, in part, thanks to the obduracy of a man with a mission, whose big idea this was. It was passed, however, at enormous political cost.

Commentators from both the right and the left predicted that these reforms would prove this government's 'poll tax' (the radical idea for a new form of local taxation that became a key factor in the downfall of Margaret Thatcher) and that it could cost the Coalition the next election.

The lessons are obvious: don't do anything so radical to one of Britain's best-loved institutions when the electorate and the staff do not believe that you told them about your plans. And certainly don't do it this way.

But a thriller has to have a plot. 'Never Again' is no dry academic study, and within the plot there are misdeeds and other colourful ingredients. If, as some allege, the coalition was just doing what a Labour government would have done, it is odd to say the least to find the NHS chief executive, Sir David Nicholson, six weeks after the general election saying of what Andrew Lansley was proposing, 'This is really, really revolutionary.' The White Paper 'Liberating the NHS' was also produced far faster than any previous health White Paper and demanded such a big change of management that Nicholson said, 'You could probably see it from space.'

Conservative Party polling ahead of the 2010 general election showed that any talk of Lansley's plans for revamping the NHS did not go down well. That is hardly surprising. Timmins quotes one senior Health Department official as saying, 'Talking about reform almost seals its fate. The public hate this discussion . . . going on the *Today* programme to talk about commissioning or economic regulation of health is (a) fundamentally boring, and (b) it's not what people want to hear . . . people don't want you to talk about the wiring.' In the face of such polling evidence, the closer the Conservative Party came to the election, the less they talked about how their NHS reforms would work; the talk instead was of patient choice, rounding on bureaucrats and on putting professionals, particularly GPs, in a more responsible position. Lansley's slogan 'no decision about me without me' came with few specifics. Timmins records that 'the political strategy was to be quiet, to be emollient about the NHS', with a close adviser noting that the NHS 'was a contrast to other bits of the reform, on schools, on welfare to work and prisoner rehabilitation'. The billboard message in January 2010 promised 'Cut the deficit, not the NHS'.

Lansley has confirmed that there was a deliberate decision to stop talking about the wiring: 'I can remember it being said explicitly to me that our presentation will be radical reform on education and reassurance on health.'[13] According to some of Lansley's advisers, Timmins records, when he protested that 'he was not being allowed to set out his stall and that might lead to trouble', he was overruled. In large part as a result of these Conservative tactics, by polling day in 2010, while Labour was still thought to have the best policies on healthcare, the gap was the smallest it had been at almost any point since 1997.[14]

During the election both Lansley and Cameron, even allowing for them being in opposition, were almost irresponsibly against what the NHS management calls 're-configurations' – the merger or closure of hospital services – particularly of course in marginal constituencies. They soon realised in government that this had been a mistake, for the health service has been reconfiguring steadily ever since 1948 and must continue to do so. Lansley won considerable credit within his party – though no votes from NHS managers, nor from clinicians, who saw the need for change – for turning up in marginal seats up and down the land, promising to halt the unpopular closure of maternity units, accident and emergency departments and the like, if the Conservatives won. This was not new: Labour in opposition had used the same tactics.

Timmins gives chapter and verse on Cameron telling NHS audiences – the royal colleges of surgeons, nurses and pathologists among others – throughout 2009 that 'there will be no more of these pointless re-organisations that aim for change but instead bring chaos'. Or that 'we will not persist with the

---

13 Nicholas Timmins, *Never Again? The Story of the Health and Social Care Act 2012 – A Study in Coalition Government and Policy Making* (Institute for Government, 2012), p. 32.

14 IPSOS Mori polling 1997–2010.

top-down restructures and reorganisations of the NHS that have dominated the last decade in the NHS', causing 'terrible disruption, demoralisation and waste'. He claimed that under the Conservatives, albeit with a few qualifications, such as 'top-down' or 'pointless' or 'meddlesome', there would be no more reorganisations. 'And yes, we will immediately stop the proposed closures of vital local services that are happening under this government too.'[15]

Vain attempts have been made since to claim the 2012 legislation as being 'bottom up' but these were soon shown to be demonstrably false. Lansley also talked about 'giving' GPs budgets, or 'enabling' them – an evolutionary, even voluntary, approach, more like fundholding or practice-based commissioning, not the compulsory, revolutionary one they are now having to live with. Before the election the Conservatives were saying 'We will give GPs the power to hold patients' budgets and commission care on their behalf' – with no hint of compulsion, and giving as reassurance the retention of primary care trusts (PCTs).

GP fundholding, as has been mentioned, had been voluntary, and evolutionary under Thatcher and Major. Scrapped by Labour initially, then reintroduced in a slightly different form, as a result no consensus had built up about its strengths and weaknesses. Some GPs I know liked fundholding, others disliked it intensely.

The chairman of the NHS Alliance, which wanted GP commissioning of care, said:

On the question of whether it was going to be compulsory

---

15 Conservatives.com, May 2009.

or not, I don't know. I think they hoped that everyone would want to do it . . . I think, before the 2010 election, they thought this was a popular movement that they could re-inspire, and that it would capture the imagination of GPs.

Nigel Edwards, the former policy director for the NHS Confederation, and its acting chief executive at the time, is quoted by Timmins as saying that when he met Lansley ahead of the election, at that point 'it was an evolutionary process in which GPs would adopt this with enthusiasm and primary care trusts would wither on the vine'.

Lansley now admits that the final decision to require all GPs to be in consortia was only taken 'in late May or early June' after the 2010 general election, although 'I was always thoroughly disposed towards that anyway, because of the experience of fundholding. I didn't want us to arrive at a 50/50 split again' where half of GPs were involved and half were not. So it was that the coalition government technically endorsed compulsory commissioning without any electoral mandate.

In order to understand the 2012 legislation it is vital to recognise that whereas the Liberal Democrats and most of the Conservative Cabinet did not really know what was going to happen, Lansley did know and so did Cameron (see pages 16, 53-54). As Timmins makes clear, Lansley had one big idea on which he never varied and which he was intent on producing. Cameron knew Lansley well, as they had worked together in the Conservative Research Department. He was complicit in the hiding of Lansley's intentions, namely to deliver, as Timmins describes it, 'the final NHS reorganisation of all time, or at least one that would last many years and could only be changed by further legislation.'[16]

Lansley knew exactly what he was doing. This is why this legislation has to be intelligently dismantled. The purity of its concept, as Timmins puts it, is simple:

> ministers would indeed remain responsible for the NHS, but rather than run it from Whitehall they would commission a set of outcomes from a national commissioning board and hold it to account for delivering them. The board would be responsible for overseeing commissioning, while itself looking after the more complex specialist services.

It was a quango wonderland gone mad. The House of Lords saw the folly of it and exposed the impossibility of Parliament and ministers withdrawing from NHS decision-making but never managed to change the actual wording of the Bill in a meaningful way. The Secretary of State for Health as a consequence does not have sufficient legal powers to act. Also the legislation ducks out of the democratic dilemma of who decides: the managers? Ministers? GPs? Foundation trusts? The whole thing is a predictable mess and it gets worse month by month. An NHS on which the inevitable rationing of care can be maintained because the public see it as broadly democratic, fair and just is disappearing before our eyes. Instead more and more doctors, GPs in particular, feel vulnerable, seeing themselves set up to take the blame when things go wrong,

---

16 Jeremy Paxman asked Lansley on *Newsnight*: 'Can you guarantee that if this Bill goes through it will be the last reform of the NHS that you can foresee for the next ten years?' Lansley replied: 'Yes.'

with the politicians and the managers going along with this sleight of hand.

The new economic regulator, which keeps the old name 'monitor', is another example of sleight of hand. It is now designed to ensure that competition law is applied across the NHS to facilitate choice and competition. The Secretary of State, major crises aside, is in theory meant to stand back and simply let it all work itself out, allowing it to run what some in the department were later to dub a 'clockwork universe', or as one of Cameron's advisers labelled it, 'this perfectly incentivised, perpetual motion machine'. I called the 2012 legislation the Secretary of State for Health's 'Abdication Bill'. The present incumbent thrashes around pretending to have powers which have been taken away, attempting to defuse crises and abusing his critics. It is not credible to continue through the next parliament with this legislation unchanged.

The shadow Health spokesman from 2010 was Andy Burnham. I hope he will be Health Secretary if Labour are in government after the 2015 general election, because he is thankfully not part of the Labour legacy of Tony Blair, Alan Milburn and Patricia Hewitt. It is to Burnham's credit, who had come in as Labour's Secretary of State for Health in 2009, that he announced that far from continuing the previous policy of extending competition for NHS services, NHS organisations were to be the services' 'preferred provider' and they were to be given a first and then a second chance to improve before their services would ever be put out to tender.

Andrew Lansley's obsession with removing this ministerial discretion over all these structures triumphed to the very end, as I discovered when negotiating with the Conservative Health spokesman in the House of Lords. We talked, but Lansley held the veto and the Cabinet and Liberal Democrats, for all their claims, never achieved any fundamental watering down of his vision. His fundamental belief comprised autonomy and a doctrine of non-intervention. His successor, Jeremy Hunt, has felt forced to intervene on many occasions, however, running a serious risk in the process of acting *ultra vires*. To counter challenges in court and to preserve the myth that NHS England is acting voluntarily, not under orders from himself, Hunt meets every Monday with NHS England's chief executive and a course is set. But the law remains in place and the ministerial separation is planned to come back into play after the general election.

At the 2010 general election the three main parties' manifestos all agreed on reducing management costs and making efficiency savings. Labour, as the government party, promised to 'cut red tape' and make £20 billion of efficiency savings. The Conservatives promised a 30 per cent, or £4.5 billon, cut in the cost of NHS administration. The Liberal Democrats promised to halve the size of the Department of Health, to scrap strategic health authorities, and to replace PCTs with elected local health boards. Labour promised an 'active role' for the independent sector, specifying 'end of life care and cancer services'. Patients requiring elective care, which in the main covers surgical operations, would 'have the right, in law, to choose from any provider who meets NHS standards of quality at NHS costs'. The Conservatives promised 'every patient the power to choose any healthcare provider that meets NHS standards, within NHS prices'. The Liberal Democrats said their local health boards would have the freedom to commission services 'from a range of different providers, including for example staff cooperatives, on the basis of a level playing field in any competitive tendering – ending any current bias in favour of private providers'.

During the election Norman Lamb, who is now the Liberal Democrat minister in the Department of Health, dismissed Lansley's independent commissioning board as 'crazy' and 'a nonsense'. 'To have an independent, non-elected quango responsible for £100 billion of public money is simply incredible,' he wrote in the *Financial Times* and even added that the Liberal Democrats would not back that in the event of a minority government.[17]

Over the course of their five days of negotiation, the coalition parties reached agreement on the NHS. 'The parties agree that funding for the NHS should increase in real terms in each year of the parliament, while recognising the impact this decision would have on other departments.' Timmins records a senior Liberal Democrat saying:

> We didn't have any other discussions about the NHS of any kind during those few days. We didn't discuss reform. I think if I'm honest the assumption probably was that the NHS was going to be an area where a degree of stability would be expected. NHS reform hadn't been one of our lead areas within our manifesto so there were no policies that we were particularly looking to promote ourselves. It wasn't one of our key negotiating areas. The Tories didn't mention anything about the NHS during the talks other than the budget situation. And therefore I think there was

17 *Financial Times*, 29 April 2010.

probably an assumption on both sides, or certainly our side, that what we would be seeing on the NHS is incremental change within the tramlines set by existing policy.

The tramlines setting policy were to be Lansley's. He at least must have been aware of the old limerick:

There once was a man who said 'Damn!
It is borne in upon me I am
An engine that moves
In predestinate grooves;
I'm not even a bus, I'm a tram.'

Maurice E. Hare (1886–1967)

The coalition then set about preparing a detailed 'programme for government'.[18] Oliver Letwin, minister for government policy and the son of a conservative philosopher, and Danny Alexander, who at that stage was Secretary of State for Scotland and Nick Clegg's adviser, came together to guide the process. Alexander later became Chief Secretary to the Treasury. Some years before I had met Letwin for lunch to discuss the NHS internal market, only to discover he felt it was wishy-washy reform and instead appeared to be in favour of a total private market in health. Their coalition document covered no fewer than thirty-one policy areas. There was to be no lack of political ambition, nor any humility that neither party had a proper electoral mandate. Its first and most notable pledge – which would not be fulfilled – was to eliminate the deficit over a parliament, twice as fast

---

18 HM Government, 'The Coalition: Our Programme for Government', 19 May 2010.

as Labour had planned and a target which Labour has over the whole parliament attacked as being too austere. In reality, despite Conservative boasting of courageously holding onto this pledge, we have sensibly ended up with something pretty close to what Alastair Darling wanted when Chancellor of the Exchequer but was not allowed to mention by Gordon Brown during the election period.

The programme for government, according to Timmins, was an entirely political exercise within No. 10. Health Department civil servants – who were already working feverishly away on Lansley's grand plan – were not involved in any way. Nor was the new Health Secretary given much chance for input. 'I did have conversations with Oliver Letwin from time to time,' Lansley says. Paul Burstow, the Liberal Democrat who had unexpectedly displaced Norman Lamb as the incoming care services minister at the Department of Health, described himself as merely 'a consultee' on the programme for government, certainly not a 'co-producer . . . it was very much those two people [Letwin and Alexander] who were leading it'.

This lack of wider consultation over the programme for government, and lack of involvement of departmental civil servants, applied in other areas. An all-smiling government in its early months was in fact almost dictatorial in its policy formation. But there was an extra factor – nobody in No. 10, or anywhere else in the top of government, knew much about government. Cameron had never been a government minister, not even the most junior. Despite extolling the merits for others of serving an apprenticeship, he had not done so himself. It was a dubious distinction he shared with two other Prime Ministers, Ramsay Macdonald in 1924 and Tony Blair in 1997.

Lansley had at least as a civil servant watched Norman Tebbit in government, not a bad model for achieving his objectives. As he said to Timmins:

We made no bones about it, and David [Cameron] was very clear about it. He had people in post across government who he intended would come into office with the reform agenda mapped out. And he was a direct participant in it. He launched the paper on outcomes not targets in 2006, he launched the Autonomy and Accountability paper in 2007.

Oliver Letwin also understood Lansley's plan, but at a somewhat high level according to Timmins.

For him the devolution of commissioning to GPs and the use of choice and competition were all part of a much wider philosophy of government that travelled at various times under various labels – from Cameron's 'big society: not big government' to Letwin's preferred formulation of 'government in a post-bureaucratic age'.

Lansley's plans in Letwin's eyes were all part of this. But Letwin would never have claimed to be a health expert, any more than Danny Alexander would.

The deliberations on the NHS over the Monday, Tuesday and Wednesday of the week beginning 16 May are described by Timmins as, according to taste, 'a spatchcocked mess'; a neat synthesis of the two parties' opposing philosophies (markets versus democracy); or, as one No. 10 insider has put it, 'a cut and shut' job (the process where the good back half of a crashed car is welded to the good front half of another wreck to produce a vehicle that may look roadworthy but is in fact potentially lethal). Or as another No. 10 insider describes the outcome, with the benefit of hindsight, a 'half-horse/half-donkey'. Yet this product and what emerged later in legislative form has to be maintained, we are told, at all costs. There can be no change after the general election in 2015 without disaster! A car that has crashed, that is totally unsafe, must nevertheless be kept running come what may – an absurd claim. NHS legislation put on the statute book by a *hung* House of Commons and a supine House of Lords with no conceivable popular mandate deserves to be changed by a combination of reinstatement and repeal.

The health section of the coalition's 'Programme for Government' contained much that had been in the Conservative manifesto, plus one item that had not: 'We will stop the top-down reorganisations of the NHS that have got in the way of patient care.' This was added as a coalition commitment, a Liberal Democrat commitment as much as a Conservative one, and one which is now proven to have been totally false.

Worse was yet to come. In the heady post-election atmosphere, Cameron and Clegg went over the top in their foreword to the 'Programme for Government' by choosing to highlight the NHS section, and wrote:

A combination of our parties' best ideas and attitudes has produced a programme for government that is more radical and comprehensive than our individual manifestos . . . For example, in the NHS, take Conservative thinking on markets, choice and competition and add to it the Liberal Democrat belief in advancing democracy at a much more local level, and you have a united vision for the NHS that is truly radical: GPs with authority over commissioning; patients with much more control; elections for your local NHS health board. Together, our ideas will bring an emphatic end to the bureaucracy, top-down control and centralisation that has so diminished our NHS.'[19]

Neither Lansley nor the department were given any satisfaction in changing words in the 'Programme for Government' and they regarded it, Timmins reports, quite simply as 'a disaster'. They knew the pledge to stop the 'top-down reorganisations of the NHS' would be a phrase that was destined to haunt the debate about the NHS reforms throughout their parliamentary life. The electorate will decide in 2015 whether they were deceived over the NHS in 2010.

On the proposed arrangements for PCTs, 'it was almost impossible to conceive of a worse piece of policy making, really,' one official said. 'Every single element of the proposal is crazy.' On top of all this there was the understandable wish of the Liberal Democrats for a fixed-term parliament. Five years was decided on by Osborne in the first few days, perhaps because he feared the Liberal Democrats would jump ship once the economic policies on the deficit began to make themselves felt.

---

19 HM Government. 'The Coalition: Our programme for Government', 19 May 2010.

Chapter 2

Fatally Flawed NHS Legislation

The NHS, like most institutions in the United Kingdom, evolved. In 1911 David Lloyd George, as Chancellor of the Exchequer, brought forward the legislation to introduce national insurance, and for the next thirty-five years public and parliamentary debate on welfare reform was dominated by the issues surrounding insurance-based healthcare, such as the exclusions from insurance cover, and the two classes of patients: those on the 'panel' and those who paid for private health. In 1920 the Minister of Health's Consultative Council on Medical and Allied Services produced the Dawson report, which, against conventional wisdom, asserted that 'the best means of maintaining health and curing disease should be made available to all citizens'. In 1926 the Royal Commission on National Health Insurance argued for 'divorcing the medical service entirely from the insurance system' and supporting it from 'the general public funds'.

In March 1943 Ernest Brown, then Minister of Health in the wartime coalition, presented proposals to Parliament for a unified healthcare system based on large local government areas, which was opposed by many in the medical profession. In February 1944 Brown's successor, Henry Willink, presented a somewhat different White Paper, which he then modified before the general election in 1945. In March 1946 'The National Health Service Bill: Summary of the Proposed New Service' was presented to Parliament, and after a long battle, including British Medical Association (BMA) opposition, and some crucial compromises, on 5 July 1948 the NHS came into existence.

In 2010, sixty-two years later, following a steady process of evolution and despite many changes, the NHS was still recognisably the same entity as that introduced by the Attlee government. That is not something to be ashamed of. The Bank of England has evolved in structure and in format in the same way, despite a mistaken attempt to deprive it of its regulatory function in 1997, thankfully now restored. So have the three armed services, though greatly reduced in size since a sensible process began under Prime Minister Harold Macmillan to create a single Secretary of State of Defence and an overall Chief of the Defence Staff. The 1947 Town and Country Planning Act is another Attlee government landmark that still remains, albeit threatened by some recent ill-advised planning reforms. A nation's identity, particularly that of the UK, relies on the fact that at its core there are powerful elements of continuity.

My father was a general practitioner, and so were my great-uncle and two of my aunts. I started off in medicine wanting to be a GP, though I ended up specialising in the brain. I have from my medical student days been an NHS reformer, publishing a book called *A Unified Health Service* as long ago as 1968. Part of the compromise over the foundation of the NHS in 1948 was that GPs were to remain independent contractors within the NHS, not salaried employees. They have always had much to contribute to NHS decision-making from that position of independence; they represent a unique feature of the NHS. But they are not the whole NHS, and they know it. Going in and out of hospital is part of the to and fro of treatment. Healthcare is a team effort. Long since gone are the hierarchical days when the single consultant or GP totally dominated NHS decision-making. They are, with nurses, dentists, radiographers, midwives and so on, part of a team and a part of an integrated healthcare system which includes social workers, physiotherapists, speech therapists, mental health specialists and a rich mixing of medical scientists and technologists.

In many university graduation ceremonies the World Health Organization (WHO) Geneva Declaration, which endorses a modern Hippocratic oath, is recited by all new members of the health professions. The new oath is more general than the original, but it is still a call to vocation; a check on behaviour. During fourteen years as chancellor of the University of Liverpool I loved presiding over this degree ceremony. It breaks my heart to contemplate the slow erosion of the vocational calling that has been at the core of healthcare over so many centuries in the UK and worldwide.

Yet no profession based on natural sciences can expect to be exempt from financial realities. In 1976 after two years as minister of health under Barbara Castle I wrote a book, *In Sickness and in Health*, which argued: 'The medical profession clearly does make economic decisions. It is not only this that should be more openly recognised, but also the considerable

21

size of the resources influenced by doctors' decisions.'[20] The previous year we had sought to reduce inequalities in the allocation of resources to regional health authorities, introducing the Resource Allocation Working Party, and we focused on 'Cinderella' areas like mental illness. But the most significant political change was that as a minister I began to openly talk and write about a rationed health service, firstly because I believed then and believe even more today that it is an inescapable fact, and also because politicians will carry more conviction over difficult choices if rationing is recognised openly and directly. For unless politicians admit this constraint on choice to the health professions, who have always known it to be true, they will find it hard to convince health professionals that political reforms of the NHS are based on realities. Without that admission, health professionals will suspect, with some justification, that political reforms are merely attempts to disguise the inevitability of rationing.

The professions have become, not unreasonably, more than a little tired of politicians boasting about the NHS being the best in the world while not recognising areas in which it has dropped down the league tables of international comparisons, nor the financial pressure placed on the NHS which works against maintaining high standards of care and the striving for excellence.

I have never therefore been a believer in the status quo for the NHS. If we manage to reinstate our NHS we must also renew it. What I hope for is continued evolution in the NHS to keep

---

20 David Owen, *In Sickness and in Health: The Politics of Medicine* (Quartet, 1976), p. 81.

pace with the radical changes in the provision of healthcare for an ageing population whose extended lifespan is in large part due to the advances brought about by the NHS. The tragedy for many reformers, like myself, has been that the internal market we advocated to bring to bear some of the financial disciplines necessary in any large organisation became a Trojan horse for an external market. Any efficient healthcare system needs to have the capacity to make cost comparisons, to experiment in different methods of working and cost controls, and to develop other techniques of good management. Unfortunately the zealots, mainly outside the NHS, took over the language of the internal market through a series of steps which became the precursor of the full-blown external market that emerged into the light of day with the coalition 2012 legislation.

As so often when analysing the future, one has to draw on the past. There is no better place to start than an article by the social historian Sally Sheard, 'Quacks and Clerks'.[21] It shows how successive Whitehall efficiency reviews between 1979 and 1994 merged the parallel medical and civil service reporting lines in the Department of Health. The effect was to reduce the Chief Medical Officer's ability to call directly upon the support of medical civil servants. Between 1960 and 1973 Sir George Godber, whose brother was a Conservative MP, became the most influential CMO to advise ministers, whether Labour or Conservative. He insisted on having direct line management of the medical civil servants, who by 1968 numbered 127 in the DHSS and 62 in the regions. Godber ensured that

---

21 Sally Sheard, 'Quacks and Clerks: Historical and Contemporary Perspectives on the Structure and Function of the British Medical Civil Service', *Social Policy and Administration* 44/2, 2010, pp. 193–207.

medical expertise was acknowledged and medical policy was appropriately developed, by obliging the parallel hierarchies to agree recommendations before they could go forward to ministers, or present divided counsel. That was the system which operated when I was minister of state for Health in 1974–6.

Sheard recalls that Margaret Thatcher is reputed to have known the exact number of doctors working in the DHSS in 1979 and to have told Patrick Jenkin, her new Secretary of State, that one of his first objectives should be to send many of them 'back to the NHS to do proper jobs'. In its contempt for coherent management it may prove one of the most costly 'penny wise, pound foolish' moments in the history of NHS management. It also defied the judgement of Thatcher's own ideological 'guru', Sir Keith Joseph, who had endorsed parallel hierarchies when he was in charge as Secretary of State for Health and was introducing legislation in the early 1970s for a three-tier reorganisation.

There were eight reviews of the department's medical staff numbers between 1981 and 1994. A further restructuring in 1995 led the former CMO Sir Donald Acheson to tell the 1998 inquiry into the bovine spongiform encephalopathy outbreak that it had left staff numbers so low that it was difficult to see how any future CMO could discharge his responsibility effectively or 'successfully insist, against opposition, on any necessary changes to address any new problems or emergencies'. Another CMO, Professor Kenneth Calman, only half-jokingly claimed his staff now consisted of a secretary and a mobile phone. Today NHS England, Monitor and the Care Quality Commission have more than four and a half times as many civil servants as the Department of Health.

The medical profession and the royal colleges in particular during this time did not live up to their Royal Charter obligations and did not maintain their professional independence. This issue came out into the open when it was revealed how the royal colleges had failed to stand up to Sir Liam Donaldson, the CMO between 1998 and 2010, the Secretary of State and ministers in the Department of Health over the 2007 Medical Training Application Service (MTAS) scandal. It was a disgrace that these proposed reforms to the training and career paths of young hospital doctors were supported unconditionally by the royal colleges. Many young consultants to this day hold them in contempt for their readiness to sell out professional standards. The General Medical Council is no better, although mainly in other areas of its responsibility.

On 16 October 2008 in an after-dinner speech at the Royal College of Physicians following Professor Sir Michael Rawlins's Harveian Oration, I warned of the perils of being embraced by the Department of Health and then of incorporation. Judging from the supportive comments afterwards, many present were aware of the need to avoid this happening again. But in 2010 the royal colleges, instead of formally consulting their members on the professional aspects, not the politics, of the Health and Social Care Bill when its framework first became known, left it to the BMA to deal with the CMO and the Secretary of State. It was yet another indication that the colleges had become too close to the department and were losing their precious independence and authority. Eventually, many were forced by their rank-and-file members to consult, and this revealed that a massive gap had developed. Although the membership were highly critical of the government legislation, their criticism came far too late to have any effect and an attempt to do so in which I was involved failed at the last moment.

Fortunately there were some exceptions. The then president of the Royal College of Ophthalmologists, Professor Harminder Dua, wrote to me on 23 January 2012 saying:

Commissioning, as it is being inferred, will introduce unfair competition in which major teaching hospitals are likely to be disadvantaged. Willing providers are likely to bid for the 'lucrative procedures' leaving hospitals to deal with the complex procedures, which in turn are inadequately funded as per current tariffs. This particularly applies to ophthalmology where cataract surgery is being diverted to independent providers who do not provide training. In some centres there aren't enough cataracts left to fulfil the training needs. The number of cataract operations performed by consultant ophthalmologists too is dropping leading to deskilling. Equally importantly, the income generated from the volume of cataract surgery is used to subsidise more complex procedures whilst still retaining a positive financial balance. Loss of this volume of cataract surgery will have significant negative knock on effects on other complex procedures disadvantaging patients.

Another potential serious consequence is the risk that emphasis will shift from providing holistic care to patients to 'organ based care'. Different services will be commissioned from possibly the cheapest providers. This will mean that patients have to travel to one centre for one type of treatment and to another centre for another treatment affecting a different organ. In ophthalmology several patients have more than one condition affecting the eye for example diabetes and cataract and glaucoma, glaucoma and cataract, macular degeneration and cataract or glaucoma. If different conditions are commissioned from different providers the patients will have to move around. This will require very efficient communication between centres to avoid duplication of medication and other intervention.

Dua drew my attention to the effect in ophthalmology of

arbitrary thresholds of visual acuity being set for cataract surgery. Thresholds for the first and second eye are different with a greater loss of vision being required before surgery can be considered for the second eye. The thresholds that are set have no scientific basis whatsoever and are purely determined by the number of cataract procedures that can be deferred to meet the savings targets. Moreover, the thresholds are variable across the country creating a post code lottery. The variable thresholds being set by different PCTs/Commissioners is further proof that these are based on financial rather than clinical needs. This is depriving many deserving patients from necessary surgery. Certain procedures such as lid warts and benign growths are being banned altogether without any alternative options being offered to patients.

If this is what the future of the NHS will look like then the Bill has serious problems. If this reflects the gap between the spirit of the Bill and its implementation then greater clarity is required in the form of explicit instructions to commissioning groups.

There are many ways in theory of reasserting professional advice and professional standards in the NHS. A place to start might well be in considering three documents. First, Harry Burns's article 'Health Tsars'[22] concluded that these tsars had proved their effectiveness because they were practising clinicians. Second, an interesting report for the National Institute for Health Research[23] praised what its authors called high-impact leaders who brought an appropriate scale of ambition and a set of micro-political capabilities to bear so as to achieve significant cross-boundary service redesign. Third, a different, but no less important, study going far wider than the NHS sees this development as 'here to stay but [needing] more transparency'.[24] It shows how tsars have become a major source of external expertise that many ministers draw upon and that their influence in Whitehall has grown progressively more significant over the last fifteen years although transparency about their work is patchy. The majority of the 260 tsars they reviewed were found to have made useful contributions. But tsars are no substitute for the day-to-day discipline of a parallel hierarchy system within the Department of Health influencing ministers in their decision-making. The department by 2015 will be a shadow of its former self in impact and authority.

The concept of an internal market in the NHS has become

---

22 Harry Burns, 'Health Tsars', *British Medical Journal*, 15 January 2004, pp 117–18.

23 John Storey and Richard Holti, 'Possibilities and Pitfalls for Clinical Leadership in Improving Service Quality, Innovation and Productivity' (National Institute for Health Research, January 2013).

24 Prof. Ken Young, Dr Ruth Levitt and William Solesbury, 'Policy tsars: here to stay but more transparency needed', King's College London, 15 October 2013, available at http://www.kcl.ac.uk/sspp/departments/politicaleconomy/research/tsars.aspx (accessed 3 November 2014).

very controversial but when it first emerged in the early 1980s with the writings of Professor Alain Enthoven of the Stanford School of Business in California, it was much less so. I described some of his ideas in my book *Our NHS*[25] and some others were adopted by the Social Democratic Party (SDP). Interestingly, we were then criticised from within the government during 1986 by the Health Service Management Board. An exchange in December 1987 of minutes between officials had one writing: 'I am still doubtful whether an Enthoven-style model would give sufficient voice to the consumer – the patient.'[26]

The SDP saw some of Enthoven's ideas as a means to improve quality in the NHS and ensure that the whole population benefited from more efficient and cost-effective NHS care. Under later SDP proposals district health authorities (DHAs) were to be 'free to contract with other DHAs and with the private and voluntary sectors'[27] in order to meet their obligations, but it was implicit in this that the NHS would be the main provider of care, with a contestability where NHS provision was failing patients.

On 28 January 1988 after winning a third general election, during which the NHS had largely escaped from the Conservatives' radical reform programme elsewhere, the Prime Minister, Margaret Thatcher, set up a small ministerial group under her chairmanship to review the NHS. The members were the Chancellor of the Exchequer, Nigel Lawson, and his number two, John Major, and the Secretary of State for Health

---

25 David Owen, *Our NHS* (Pan, 1988), pp. 102–8.

26 Quoted in Brian Edwards and Margaret Fall, *The Executive Years of the NHS: The England Account 1985–2003* (Radcliffe, 2005), p.57.

27 *The NHS: The Next 40 Years* (SDP, 1988), pp. 14–15.

and Social Security, John Moore, and his number two, Tony Newton. Moore and Newton were both later replaced by Ken Clarke and David Mellor when Health was split off from Social Security. The five met once a week and subsequently more often, their meetings culminating in the publication of the January 1989 White Paper 'Working for Patients'. This paper marked the official start of the internal market within the NHS.

In his autobiography Nigel Lawson describes the discussions on the ministerial committee and makes clear why their conclusions did not embrace privatisation. A self-confessed 'arch promoter of privatisation', he writes: 'The provision of medical care is sui generis, and should not be assimilated to other activities where full-blooded privatization is entirely appropriate.'[28] He established a clear demarcation line and went on to develop some guidelines about the economics of healthcare. 'Simply stated, the demand for healthcare exceeds the supply.' He also tried to draw another clear demarcation, arguing against making all personal subscriptions to BUPA and similar private health insurance schemes tax deductible. If we simply boost demand, he claimed, for example by tax concessions to the private sector, without improving supply, the result would not be so much a growth in private healthcare but higher prices. The key for him was in the supply side. His concession of providing tax relief on personal private medical insurance premiums, but limiting this to the over-sixties, had been wrung out of him by Thatcher, but was abolished by Labour in 1997. It has not been changed since and seems now to have become an established demarcation line

---

28 Nigel Lawson, *The View from No. 11: Memoirs of a Tory Radical* (Bantam, 1992), pp. 615–16.

across all the main political parties, making it easier for public and private medicine to coexist (see pp. 210-212).

Following on from the introduction of general management when Norman Fowler was secretary of state, a sense was created that a degree of separation between purchasers and providers was an effective way of bringing more market disciplines into the NHS and it was argued as being compatible with its founding principles. But this separation was not without its dangers and, in fairness, some health commentators did see this. On the cost-effective evidence so far they have been proved correct.

The idea that GPs might hold budgets for patient care emerged during the 1980s, led in the UK by academics including Alan Maynard and Marshall Marinker, and was taken up by Kenneth Clarke during the 1989 NHS review that led to 'Working for Patients'. Other academics in the 1990s saw the dangers ahead and warned of them, prominent during the Labour government was Professor Allyson Pollock. Initially, GP fundholding was rolled out by John Major's government. Entirely voluntary, it had the merit of making those GPs who chose to involve themselves far more aware of the costs associated with the allocation of resources, but it blurred the line between purchasers and providers, particularly as fundholding practices undertook an increasing range of services in house during the 1990s. But this, it was argued, was not always a bad thing, and was an inevitable consequence of involving GPs.

The continued popularity across the political spectrum of some systems of GP budget-holding suggested that it was a worthwhile strategy, and if well conceived, compatible with a pragmatic voluntary internal market. However, it presented a model of integrated health management that bore some resemblance to health maintenance organisation setups elsewhere, not least the oft-cited model embodied in Kaiser Permanente, America's largest not-for-profit healthcare organisation, which combines both the commissioning and the provision of care for millions of subscribers.[29]

The bringing together of many small GP practices in fundholding, and the later development of total purchasing pilots for the largest fundholding groups to commission the full range of care, rather than the limited range available to most fundholding GPs, never really came to prove their worth as they came very late in the Conservatives' final term of office. Following Labour's election in 1997, despite a vague commitment to destroy the internal market in general, the concept survived, but GP fundholding initially did not. Yet Labour's system of 'practice-based commissioning' which followed bore some similarities with the earlier system. In the 1990s the NHS was unwilling or unable to invest in information systems, and the practice of adjusting prices for the different intensities of care within a single diagnosis, known as 'casemix', was in its infancy. This made quality measurement difficult, except for the crude mortality and waiting time statistics incorporated into the Patient's Charter.

By 1992 I had ceased to be an MP and for three years I was half-jokingly referring to myself as undergoing penal servitude as the EU peace negotiator in the former Yugoslavia. During this period I was away from the UK most of the time, days would pass without my seeing an English newspaper or TV, and I was

---

29 Richard G. A. Feachem, Neelam K. Sekhri and Karen L. White, 'Getting More for Their Dollar: A Comparison of the NHS with California's Kaiser Permanente, *British Medical Journal*, 19 January 2002, pp. 135–43.

reliant on the *International Herald Tribune* and the BBC World Service. Then I became a serious businessman and my infrequent speeches in the House of Lords were mainly devoted to foreign affairs. I was not devoting my part-time political activities to the NHS and was remiss in not picking up that the internal market was being traduced in a direction that I and many others had never expected nor would ever support. I had established a cross-party campaigning organisation in 1999 called Open Europe, which while fully supporting EU membership was opposed to the UK entering the eurozone. There was a political danger in 2003 of Tony Blair on the back of what was referred to in No. 10 as the forthcoming 'Baghdad Bounce' holding a referendum on taking the UK into the euro. Fortunately (only in this regard) there was no public opinion poll 'bounce' and the whole Iraq venture was a bigger disaster than even the 1956 invasion of Suez. Largely as a consequence I was able to wrap up Open Europe in 2005 when it was obvious that adopting the euro was off the political agenda for decades. But still I did not really engage with the NHS.

On 12 September 2007 the then Prime Minister, Gordon Brown, asked me to become involved with the NHS in his government. That invitation had its origin, looking back, in what had happened a fortnight earlier, when on 29 August Nelson Mandela's statue was unveiled on the south-west corner of Parliament Square. For years I had been on the committee responsible for a memorial, initially at the invitation of the South African journalist Donald Woods. Woods had been a friend of Steve Biko, the leader of the Black Consciousness movement who was brutally killed by the police on 13 September 1977 while in custody. Biko's death and the worldwide sense of outrage at the circumstances of his dying, handcuffed and in leg irons, travelling naked for more than 700 miles in the back of a Land-Rover with a beaten head and severely bruised brain, meant that together with the US Secretary of State, Cyrus Vance, I as Foreign Secretary was able to overcome the resistance in London and go across the all-important political threshold in the UN Security Council in November 1977, when the apartheid policies of South Africa were declared a threat to peace and a mandatory arms embargo was applied. This led slowly but inexorably to the banking sanctions which forced President de Klerk to free Mandela in January 1990.

The day of the unveiling had started with breakfast at a hotel with Mandela organised by Richard Attenborough. Dickie had been a stalwart supporter of the SDP and a good social democrat, and had like many others gone back to the Labour Party when it started to reform itself. We were still friends and he made sure I sat next to Mandela, which was a total delight. Gordon Brown, who had only become Prime Minister a few months previously, made an excellent speech, straight from the heart. As I listened I hoped he would do well but I still worried about the fundamentals of New Labour after the debacle following the invasion of Iraq in 2003.

I started to walk down Whitehall to a reception at the Banqueting Hall. Suddenly a surprisingly tall young man joined me and started chatting to me. It was Ed Miliband. We had never met before but as we talked I found a highly intelligent politician who I instantly liked. I started after this, as so often happens following a chance meeting, to read and listen to more of what he was saying, and he began to stand out in my mind among younger Labour politicians, along with Ed Balls. Balls, solidly against the euro, is a Norwich City supporter and with Delia Smith we meet up.

A short while later, apparently out of the blue, I was asked to see Gordon Brown urgently. A meeting was fixed for the evening of Wednesday 12 September before I flew next day on business to Chicago. I imagine, though I never asked Gordon, that we were meeting in part at the instigation of Ed Miliband. Only the day before, with great publicity, Brown had seen Margaret Thatcher in 10 Downing Street. In our long conversation it became pretty clear that Gordon Brown wanted me to advise him on the NHS, in effect as part of his GOAT – government of all the talents – initiative. It was tempting but for many good reasons it was not something that I was ready to undertake. Devoted though I have always been to the NHS, I doubted I would have had real influence, since a new Secretary of State, Alan Johnson, had been appointed 2½ months earlier. My service in the former Yugoslavia between 1992 and 1995 meant that I had taken a big step back from domestic politics. Since 1996 I had been chairman of a public company investing in a Russian steel plant. My knowledge of the NHS was much less than when Minister of Health under Barbara Castle in the big super-ministry, the Department of Health and Social Security, from 1974 to 1976. Labour also seemed to have moved too far, under Tony Blair and Alan Milburn, from 1999 until 2003, away from the internal market which I had espoused in the mid-1980s. There was a part of me that was disillusioned with New Labour over Iraq. I was content to remain an independent crossbencher in the House of Lords. I had thought that New Labour might carry the flag for what the SDP should have been; in 1997 their achievements with devolution in the UK and peace initiatives over Ireland augured well. But I had declined Tony Blair's specific invitation to rejoin in the summer of 1996, in part because I did not share his enthusiasm for the euro after hearing for myself how little he knew about the intrinsic flaws in its design.

Eventually, I was glad Blair was pushed in 2006 to resign by Labour MPs within a year, yet my good friends who had served the Blair government had long been very critical of Gordon Brown. They believed that he was not going to be a good Prime Minister. Always an optimist, I did not share their views and hoped he would take Labour closer to social democracy. They said that I was too positive about his personality and his style of working, and that he was too embroiled in the presidential model after having in effect operated a joint presidency, at the expense of the Cabinet, with Tony Blair.

On the Friday evening after my meeting with Brown, while travelling between Chicago and Athens, I was being inundated with telephone calls from Sunday newspaper journalists who had been variously briefed by No. 10 that we had talked and that I was returning to the Labour Party. I had to correct the impression that I was rejoining Labour, which was untrue, while indicating, which was true, that I wished Gordon Brown well personally and hoped he would be a successful Prime Minister. Everyone expected him to call an immediate general election but to my disappointment, having marched his men to the top of the hill like the Duke of York, he marched them down again. It looked like a lack of nerve at the point of decision.

Later during the banking crisis of 2008 the UK seemed to be benefiting from Brown's long Treasury experience. He gathered around him a good team for the G20 summit in London and wisely used the international experience of Lord

Malloch-Brown, a senior UN diplomat and one-time SDP candidate, who joined as a so-called GOAT. Also successfully included as part of Brown's GOAT initiative were Lord Darzi of Denham, a distinguished surgeon who had been pioneering robotic techniques, and who added valuable expertise as a junior minister in the Department of Health, and a former Chief of the Naval Staff, Lord West of Spithead, who came in as minister for security matters. The concept, though not new, was a good one of systematically bringing in outside expertise.

The incoming Labour government in 1997 kept its promise and accepted the previous Conservative government's public expenditure forward plans. Only in its second term, after the 2001 general election, did it turn to the very necessary policy of increasing NHS spending, following the review of health spending conducted by Derek Wanless. It also began to develop a more market-based agenda.

In opposition Labour had attacked the Conservatives' use of private finance initiatives (PFI) for hospital redevelopment, but went on to adopt the approach with extraordinary vigour for capital projects, even though they would place significant financial burdens on local health systems in order to meet the astronomical costs of using private finance.[30] That government also created more than 300 PCTs, reverting to a smaller number as problems arose, with PCTs merging in order to confront budget deficits. Eventually there were 151 PCTs, similar to the number of health authorities that existed prior to Labour coming to power in 1997. Central control remained strong, with

---

30 Allyson M. Pollock, David Price and Moritz Liebe, 'Private Finance Initiatives During NHS Austerity', *British Medical Journal*, 9 February 2011.

a steady flow of instructions to PCTs from the NHS Executive.

Shortly after the 2010 general election Polly Toynbee and her husband David Walker wrote *The Verdict*, a friendly but critical assessment of Labour's record. They described the situation in health:

> The 2001 increase in National Insurance pegged explicitly to increased health spending said: better services cost more. The increase was popular.
>
> NHS spending was a Labour triumph, but with it came a fixation on the minutiae of healthcare, not just organizations and management, but operations, clinical practice and recovery rates.
>
> As in schooling, Labour ministers sitting in Whitehall could not stop themselves tinkering. Plans, reforms, edicts and reorganisations spewed out. In Scotland and Wales their absence showed how little Labour meddling mattered to patients. What mattered was more money.[31]

A 2008 Nuffield Trust study said that 'no-one could justifiably deny the past decade has seen an improvement in quality in the NHS', but added that 'given the generous increase in resources dedicated to healthcare there are many who question whether progress has been as marked, as rapid, or as predictable as might have been expected'.[32]

The Verdict blames the fact that the rate of progress fell behind

---

31 Polly Toynbee and David Walker, *The Verdict: Did Labour Change Britain?* (Granta, 2010), pp.44–5.

32 Sheila Leatherman and Kim Sutherland, *The Quest for Quality: Refining the NHS Reforms – a Policy Analysis and Chartbook* (Nuffield Trust, 2008), p. 3.

the rate of spending upon the endless cycle of reform under Tony Blair and his pro-market health ministers: 'They spent so much time and goodwill chopping and churning, refusing to admit a redoubtable truth. The NHS, big, baggy and shot through with anomalies, worked pretty well. What the anorexic patient they inherited in 1997 needed most was fattening up. Force-feeding was the wrong therapy.' It quoted the former Labour health minister Lord Warner as saying that the NHS probably received too much, too quickly.[33] Using the NHS budget alone to tackle inequalities is a strategy that is doomed to fail given that the causes of health disparities range well beyond the scope of health services alone. It also has damaging consequences for NHS patient care, because of the diversion of funds that is not justified by results.

The Verdict concluded its judgement on Labour's record over the NHS:

> After thirteen years the UK was in better health, even if the exact part played by government policies was debatable. The death rate fell by 17 per cent. Life expectancy continued its remarkable ascent. For every 100,000 of those aged under seventy-five, circulatory disease accounted for 129 deaths in 1998, but only 74 in 2007, exceeding the target Labour set themselves. Wonder drugs, such as statins, played their part, but how people ate, drank and exercised was critical . . . But the gap in life expectancy between men in poorest areas and the average grew by 2 per cent. For women the gap was worse; it widened by 11 per cent from 1997. Death rates

---

33 Toynbee and Walker, *The Verdict*, p. 45.

remained lowest in the better-off South East, worst in the North West.[34]

The independent sector treatment centres (ISTCs), which were brought in on a standard national contract from 2003 to tackle NHS waiting lists, appeared to have achieved their short-term goals, albeit at considerable expense. Some commentators have argued that the ISTCs were brought in also to serve a strategic purpose as 'a crucial step in the replacement of the NHS as an integrated public service by a healthcare market, in which private providers will play a steadily increasing role'.[35] The use of pre-paid contracts for private providers meant that many were overpaid when treatment volumes were lower than expected,[36] as a result of Patricia Hewitt's determination that ISTCs should not bear all of the risk if NHS patients should choose not to use them to the expected extent.

A problem with Labour's record and NHS policy lay with its confused ambitions on the achievement of equity. The pursuit of more equal outcomes, through a range of expensive initiatives and changes to the NHS resource allocation system, took place while health inequalities widened. Near the end of Labour's period in office in 2009 Andy Burnham, Labour's last Secretary of State for Health, in rejecting the 'any willing provider' model for NHS care and saying that for Labour 'the preferred provider' was the correct choice provided the cornerstone criticism for

---

34 Ibid., p. 49.

35 Stewart Player and Colin Leys, *Confuse and Conceal : The NHS and Independent Sector Treatment Centres* (Merlin Press, 2008), p. 71.

36 D. Martin, 'How Labour blew £250 million on private surgery that never took place', *Daily Mail*, 10 March 2011.

many people, including myself, of the later Lansley reforms of 'any willing provider'.

In 2010 the coalition agreement on health changed Gordon Brown's preferred-provider policy for the NHS and said the new government would reinstate 'the power to choose any willing provider that meets NHS standards, within NHS prices'.[37] They were deliberately crossing a vital threshold and embarking on an external market. By then my mind was on business, not politics. I had closed down the website for Charter 2010 (see Chapter 6) and was very involved in the US with international companies in pharmaceuticals, oil, steel and iron ore in Russia. It was my family, particularly my son and daughter-in-law, both medical doctors, who virtually forced me one day to sit down and read the Health and Social Care Bill in 2011. After several hours I was shattered by how far reaching and devastating the proposals were.

Dr Sarah Wollaston, the newly elected Conservative MP for Totnes and herself a GP, was a new presence in West Country politics and was totally correct when she said, 'It does look like someone had tossed a grenade into the PCTs.'[38] In addition to the active promotion and enforcement of an NHS free market in the supply of healthcare, the Bill suggested that providers would be able to undercut applicable NHS tariff prices, thus bringing price competition into the core of the NHS. This was later slightly modified but in a way that meant it was not hard to see the direction of travel, particularly if the Conservatives

---

37 HM Government. 'The Coalition: Our Programme for Government', 19 May 2010.
38 Martin Beckford, 'Patients miss operations as government "tosses grenade" into NHS', *Daily Telegraph*, 17 January 2011.

were to win outright. This became ever clearer after Royal Assent as commissioners decided to put NHS provision out to tender, fearing criticisms from Monitor and action from private companies pressurising for contracts. Market zealotry was then curbed by the public relations skills of the new Secretary of State, Jeremy Hunt, driven by fear of the electoral consequences. But the genie of marketisation was out of the bottle. It took a little time for Labour MPs to recognise that there would have to be early emergency legislation to reverse the 2012 Act as private companies would pursue tendering even if Labour won the election and NHS England would not, and probably in most cases could not, stop the process until the law of the land was changed.

The size of some of the NHS tendering contracts became far greater than was expected. In the spring of 2014 it was announced that a ten-year contract for Staffordshire Cancer Services for adults and children, including surgery, breast screening and end-of-life care, would be tendered. Commercial companies such as Serco, UnitedHealth and Sodexo, as well as Kaiser Permanente, began to expect terms that would make any decision of an incoming government not to roll over contracts too expensive to contemplate under the Transatlantic Trade Investment Partnership treaty being negotiated between the EU and the US with its development charge.

Prior to the general election the Conservatives had earned support in the NHS community for their promises to abolish the 'target culture' and to avoid further disruptive orders from the top. Targets had been used very widely as a control mechanism under Labour, and a shift to a more advisory use for them was felt by many to provide a better balance of clinical responsibility with transparency in NHS performance. Paradoxically, however, despite these promises, and despite the coalition's commitment to cutting quangos, they went on to create the largest centrally dictating quango ever, NHS England, and then targets reappeared.

Looking for criticism in 2011 to two previously highly respected independent charities, the Nuffield Trust and the King's Fund, I found nothing published with contrary views and instead much that encouraged the process of marketisation. This was bizarre behaviour given what a health charity is supposed to uphold, objective educational standards and research. Looking back I could see that for more than a decade they had been flirting with the market seemingly without any examination of the driving forces behind it, shareholder returns and profit-driven investment.

The NHS was being destabilised and good managers began to leave. The very incoherence of the proposals shocked many fair-minded people in the NHS who sensed that integration was going to suffer from fragmentation and discontinuity of care. Friends of mine in the NHS began to look for the exit door.

The BMA was initially cautious. The King's Fund and the Nuffield Trust, while apparently enthusiastic about marketisation, focused on the sheer scale of change and potential disruption. The Nuffield Trust also warned that 'many previous reforms [of commissioning] have struggled to win the support and engagement of GPs, and this will again be a crucial issue'. Simon Stevens, formerly Blair's health adviser in Downing Street, then president of global health at UnitedHealth in the US, and now chief executive of NHS England, said that 'the proposals come ten years after Tony Blair, then Prime Minister, took the first steps down this path. What makes the coalition's proposals so radical is not that they tear up that earlier plan. It is that they move decisively towards fulfilling it'.[39] Almost, as it turned out, a job application.

Andy Burnham warned, 'Is not the handing of the public budget to independent contractors tantamount to the privatisation of the commissioning function in the NHS?' He said that the government and Lansley were

> bringing a series of market reforms into hospitals. He tells us that the first role of Monitor will be to promote competition, and he talks of any willing provider and freedoms for foundation trusts. Is not that the green light to let market forces rip right through the system with no checks or balances?[40]

The commissioning board, he claimed with justification, would be 'the biggest quango in the world' with no transparency over how it would be accountable to Parliament. To Burnham the White Paper represented overall 'a roll of the dice that puts the NHS at risk – a giant political experiment with no consultation, no piloting and no evidence'. The Health Secretary was 'removing public accountability and opening the door to unchecked privatisation'. It would 'turn order into chaos. We will oppose it,' Burnham said.

Fortunately, Dr Clare Gerada was to succeed Dr Steve Field as chairman of council of the Royal College of General Practitioners.

---

39 Simon Stevens, 'NHS reform is a risk worth taking', *Financial Times*, 15 July 2010.
40 Hansard, HC Deb, 12 July 2010, vol. 513, col. 664.

Field was broadly supportive of the principles in the White Paper, while accepting that his membership had divided views. Soundings showed that the college's younger GPs were appreciably keener on the idea of taking control of the budget than its older members. Responding to the White Paper, the college said, 'Our members are enthusiastic about the opportunity for GPs to play a leading role in shaping services for their patients.' But that headline support for the principle was heavily caveated by worries about what it would do to the doctor–patient relationship, the 'proposed scale, pace and cost of change', the loss of PCT expertise, the 'imperative to offer choice' and 'an increased dependency on private providers'. The college was worried that 'in the context of economic strictures' GPs would be held personally responsible for consequent shortcomings in services.

Gerada herself took a tougher line, declaring, in *The Guardian* on 20 November 2010 that the reforms would mean 'the end of the NHS as we know it'. It would no longer be 'a national unified health service, with central policies and central planning in the way that Bevan imagined,' she said. Making GPs 'the new rationers' could break the bond of trust between doctors and patients. The English health system would look more and more like America's. Then at a select committee hearing, Sir David Nicholson, responded to a statement from Sarah Wollaston MP that PCTs were 'in meltdown' as staff took voluntary redundancy and the trusts were being merged into clusters. 'You are absolutely right,' Nicholson told her, adding that he was putting in place 'Stalinist' controls to keep a grip on the finances and provided the first hints that not all GP consortia would be ready by 2013 as planned and that primary care clusters might survive beyond that.

Alongside, the Health Secretary challenged his chief executive's endorsement of PCTs being 'in meltdown', but also found himself having to deny that his plans amounted to 'a nuclear device' going off inside the NHS. Later he tried to paint the reforms as anything but a revolution, arguing they were merely 'an evolution' of Labour's practice-based commissioning.[41]

As concern mounted over the reforms, Oliver Letwin and Danny Alexander held seven or eight meetings with the department, both in Richmond House and in No. 10, that eventually involved 'a cast of thousands', from Clegg and Cameron's special advisers down to departmental and Treasury officials, which went through not just the mechanics of the NHS reforms but the plans for winter. While this review was taking place, according to Nicholas Timmins, a very prescient outburst happened.

The headlines for the NHS only got worse. Robert Creighton, a highly regarded PCT chief executive who had been principal private secretary to Virginia Bottomley when she was health secretary, exploded during a conference at the King's Fund, declaring that the reforms were 'heading for a train crash'.

As health ministers, including Lansley, repeatedly attacked managers as bureaucrats and 'pen pushers' Creighton said he and his staff felt that everything they had been doing over the years was being belittled. He was doing nothing but interview people for jobs in the reshaped 'clusters' with staff doing 'nothing about patient care, money, or anything else'. The service was 'at risk of blowing

---

41 Health Select Committee hearing, 23 November 2011.

it', he said. This, he added, could be 'a bloody awful train crash. It could collapse.'

The following day finance officers at the Healthcare Financial Management Association's annual conference were treated to a lecture by Simon Burns, the minister of state for health, on how choice and competition would solve all the service's problems, before Nicholson spoke. When he did so, he produced one of the two great sound bites of the entire saga.

Nicholson said he had been consulting management gurus from around the world. 'No one could come up with a scale of change like the one we are embarking on at the moment. Someone said to me, "It is the only change management system you can actually see it from space – it is that large."' Giving GPs control of the money, he added, 'turns the whole system on its head'. His mixed message, again, was that most big change management programmes fail but that he had 'absolutely no doubt' that the NHS could deliver.[42]

The chief executive of one of Britain's biggest private hospital groups was reported by the *Financial Times* on 14 December 2010 as saying of Lansley:

If I went to my board and said that I'd told my senior management that I was merging all their posts before making them redundant in two years' time; that I'd told all my

---

42 Nicholas Timmins, *Never Again? The Story of the Health and Social Care Act 2012 – A Study in Coalition Government and Policy Making* (Institute for Government, 2012), pp. 87–8.

finance people they too will be going; and that I was going to get some other people to run the business; and that while I can't yet define it precisely, it will involve the nurses – well, I think it would be me who was out of a job.

A Letwin–Alexander review then concluded that Lansley's plans were to go ahead, provided the transition was carefully handled. The Prime Minister's view was, as so often, just to improve its public relations. But what was crystal clear was that the central thrust of the reforms – in crude terms 'pass the buck to the GPs, let them take the flak, while the politicians retreat to talking about obesity and smoking' – was dead in the water. The GPs had smelt a rat, and they realised that it was lurking in a poisoned chalice.

The reason that the Liberal Democrats did not kill the Bill is that Nick Clegg, according to an adviser, 'took the view that it would be worse for the health service to abandon it altogether than to proceed with an amended bill. The changes had gone too far. PCTs were being rolled up, people were leaving, the labour market was moving. And there was a chance that with a pause and a listening exercise we could get some of the medical profession on side – although as it turned out, of course, we didn't.'[43]

On 31 March 2011, as the Bill was finishing its committee stage, Lansley and his top officials were summoned to No. 10. Cameron read them a form of words about the pause and he slapped Lansley down when he argued. Clegg said, 'Andrew, the reason why we are here is because you have put the ideological cart before the political horse.'[44] An interesting

43 Ibid., p. 93.
44 Ibid.

revelation in that it implies that Clegg's objection was not ideological but tactical. As *The Guardian* later reported, 'it was a case of summoning a Cabinet minister to No 10, giving him a pen and notepad, and telling him what will happen'.[45] It was a humiliating episode.

Health officials were told to go away and come back within twenty-four hours with a plan to make 'the pause' work, a plan which became the Future Forum. Dr Steve Field was announced as chairman on April Fool's Day, having ceased to be chairman of the Royal College of General Practitioners the previous November. His reaction to the White Paper was: 'I liked it actually. I thought the vision was good.' Not surprisingly, therefore, his suggested changes to the Bill were politically designed to keep the Liberal Democrats on board and mainly cosmetic.

The Liberal Democrats who had the greatest reservations were Dr Graham Winyard, a former deputy chief medical officer who was chairman of the Winchester party; Dr Charles West, a popular GP and chairman of the Shrewsbury Liberal Democrats; Dr Evan Harris, an MP until the 2010 election and a former health spokesman, and a former member of council of the BMA; and Andrew George MP, a GP who represented St Ives and who courageously voted consistently against the legislation from start to finish.

On 5 May 2011, the Liberal Democrats were hammered in the local elections and lost 500 seats. At the same time the referendum on the alternative vote, for which the Liberal Democrats were firmly in the 'yes' camp, returned a resounding 'no'. It was a double rebuff from which they never recovered and

---

45 *The Guardian*, 8 April 2011.

which made many voters recall their about-turn over university tuition fees, now on proportional voting.

The so-called listening exercise through the Future Forum was a mechanism for Cameron and Clegg to accept the Forum's report, which they did together with all its recommendations bar one. But, as Timmins wrote, 'the adage that the reforms had become as much about politics as policy held true. Ahead of publication of the Future Forum's report on 13 June and the Government's response on 14 June, everyone was claiming victory.'[46] Nick Clegg briefed his backbenchers that eleven of the thirteen 'red lines' set by the Liberal Democrat spring conference had been met. 'We have achieved all we set out to achieve. It is a job well done.' The changes would take place more slowly; they would constitute evolution, not revolution, with no preference given to the private sector and proper accountability for commissioning groups, he said. 'All these things have been very, very handsomely met.'[47]

By contrast, David Cameron was telling his backbenchers that the essence of the reforms remained, including more competition, while Lansley told them that his own 'red lines' had not been crossed, and that no real ground had been conceded. This was correct: the Bill remained substantially unchanged and although at times it looked as if it would never be seen as his Bill, it will stay Lansley's and Cameron's Act until removed from the statute book.

Never Again summarises the results accurately:

---

46 Timmins, *Never Again?*, p. 99.

47 *The Guardian*, 30 June 2011.

Key conclusions from the Future Forum and the pause were that Monitor should now be not just a competition regulator but should also be charged with promoting 'integrated care' where that was in patients' best interest – 'integrated care' being a phrase subject to almost as many definitions, many of them differing, as there are letters in it.

Instead of 'promoting competition', its task was to be tackling 'anti-competitive practices'. And rather than being scrapped, the existing advisory Co-operation and Competition Panel was to be retained and transferred to Monitor.

A token hospital doctor and nurse was to be put on each commissioning group, with the idea of pure GP consortia now consigned to history.

Commissioning groups were to have proper governance and would only fully take their budgets when ready. They were now to be required to engage with a hugely expanded range of interests – patients, the local Healthwatch, local health and wellbeing boards, 'clinical senates' (newly created, but, as it turned out, non-statutory advisory bodies of specialists), along with clinical networks to advise them on integration and reconfigurations in particular specialities.[48]

The mess had become even more incoherent and the chaos that was to come in subsequent years was to a great extent a product of the Future Forum. It compounded the bureaucracy

---

48 Timmins, *Never Again?*, p. 100.

of the NHS, rather than slimming it. There were some 1,000 amendments, largely technical, such as changing the name of GP consortia to clinical commissioning groups. Ironically, Alan Milburn, the former Labour Secretary of State, who had started the movement towards an external market in 2002 told the *Daily Telegraph* the reforms were 'the biggest car crash in NHS history'.

Shortly after the Future Forum report was published, Sir Roger Boyle, the Health Department's 'heart tsar', retired, declaring he had decided to go partly because he fundamentally disagreed with the reforms. The government had been 'so busy condemning what happened before', he said, that it was not prepared to learn from what had worked well. It was 'completely baloney' to say the service was overmanaged and by 'tossing out' PCTs and strategic health authorities, corporate memory and valuable networks were being lost. This 'substantial reorganisation' was not needed, he said. He later told the BBC's *Today* programme that 'we could have got to the same point without this huge disruption . . . it is horrific that the NHS's future is threatened'.

As the Lords, to no real effect, agonised over the legislation, Professor Malcolm Grant, newly appointed as chair of the commissioning board, told the Commons Health Select Committee at his pre-appointment hearing that the Bill was 'completely unintelligible' – a performance that led to his appointment being supported by the committee only on the casting vote of Stephen Dorrell MP as its chairman. As chairman of what is now called NHS England Grant is still fighting a losing battle to make the Health and Social Care Act intelligible.

Grant summed up what the 2012 legislation means to him in an article in *The Times* on 1 April 2013. 'Something radical occurs in the NHS in England today – Parliament has transferred operational control of the health service away from politicians for the first time in its 65-year history.' When Andrew Lansley's new successor as Secretary of State, Jeremy Hunt, started to take political decisions and intervene in what was now called NHS England's area of responsibility, in order to defuse the public relations disasters that were being served up daily in the newspapers, the purists' doctrine that the sole responsibility of NHS England was to ensure the NHS used its massive budget effectively was shattered.

David Cameron's involvement before the 2010 general election is clear cut, in Timmins's analysis:

It is far from the case that the senior Conservatives – Cameron, Osborne and Letwin, for example – were ignorant about what Lansley was up to. Cameron had personally helped launch the *Autonomy and Accountability* white paper [when in opposition]. He had made plenty of speeches about the Conservatives' plans. And, as one Tory official puts it, the myriad policy papers that followed the original paper 'were written through the Oliver Letwin process' – Letwin holding a position as sort of policy overlord for Cameron's new style of Tory politics.

'Oliver held the ring on a lot this stuff,' one Conservative special adviser says. 'James O'Shaughnessy [Cameron's director of policy] would have penned quite a lot of the words. And all those things were cleared by a policy board chaired by Cameron. So the idea that Cameron didn't know what was in it . . . He and Oliver Letwin helped write the green papers.'[49]

Labour's position before the general election of 2010 had changed, according to Timmins:

> The fact was entirely visible even when Labour was in power. It is not just that much of the oomph went out of the pre-existing NHS reforms when Gordon Brown became Prime Minister. The Conservatives had watched Andy Burnham adopt his NHS 'preferred provider' approach when Health Secretary in 2009.
>
> Burnham had renewed orders for the provider arms of PCTs to be separated out in the months running up to the general election. But his preferred model was that they went to NHS trusts and foundation trusts as a way of providing integrated care, not greater competition. And Milburn and others had been attacking in public Burnham's shift to 'preferred provider', and the Brown administration going soft on competition.[50]

Labour's problem was that Ed Miliband moved Burnham away from health when he became leader. Normally this is a good thing to do in opposition but in this case it was not helpful because Labour's shift of position in government was maintained but not reinforced. That changed when Miliband wisely asked Burnham to return to the role of health spokesman.

---

49 Timmins, *Never Again?*, p. 38.
50 Ibid., p. 138.

Cameron's reaction as Prime Minister to demands that the Bill be dropped never varied. Backbenchers at a private meeting were told that there would be no retreat. The problem, he told them, was one of 'presentation not substance'[51] at a time when sources inside No. 10 were beginning to conclude gloomily that 'there is no policy solution to what is in fact a political problem. We need to reform the politics of this.' So attack became the best form of defence. Hunt was chosen for his not inconsiderable public relations skills to act as pack leader but he has not succeeded. Conservatives will demand changes to this legislation, pressured by public opinion. Douglas Carswell, MP for Clacton, who moved to UKIP, abandoned his hitherto policy of supporting an insurance based NHS and on 20 November 2014 talked on BBC TV *Question Time* of the Lansley/Cameron reforms as being 'fatally flawed' on the night that his fellow Conservative MP, Mark Reckless, won Rochester and Strood for UKIP. Even Kenneth Clarke on the same programme admitted no-one understood the Lansley reforms. These may be cynical political moves, but better repentance than obduracy. The Reinstatement campaign is working to convert MPs and candidates in all parties and none. The NHS does not belong to the political parties, in a very real sense it belongs to the people.

---

51 *Financial Times*, 15 March 2011.

Chapter 3

A People's Commission[52]

I never could have imagined after retiring from the House of Commons on the eve of the 1992 general election that I would find myself twenty-one years later at the age of seventy-four on a protest march for the NHS in south-east London. My wife and I were marching through the centre of Lewisham with our two sons and two of our four grandchildren, who all live nearby. We were protesting at the devastating changes being proposed for Lewisham Hospital. As it turned out, this march gave the momentum for a successful fightback against the destruction of our NHS as we have known it, led by local people ready to take to the street and supported by Lewisham Council and the local MPs. The story of their success was the stimulus for a slow build-up to what I hope

---

52 This chapter draws extensively on the report of the Lewisham People's Commission, quoting extensive passages from it, and I am very grateful to the editors of the report for their permission to do so. Olivia O'Sullivan and Elizabeth Woodcraft (eds), *Report of the Lewisham People's Commission*, November 2013, available online at www.savelewishamhospital.com/peoples-commission-report (accessed 21 November 2014).

will be an all-party campaign within the general election.

The Lewisham protest began in July 2012 when the then Secretary of State for Health, Andrew Lansley, appointed a trust special administrator (TSA), Matthew Kershaw, to take over South London Healthcare Trust, which had developed severe financial difficulties. The trust consisted of Queen Elizabeth Hospital, Woolwich (QEH), in the London Borough of Greenwich; Princess Royal University Hospital, Orpington (PRUH), in the London Borough of Bromley; and Queen Mary's Hospital, Sidcup (QMH), in the London Borough of Bexley.

The staff at Lewisham Hospital, in the London Borough of Lewisham, and the local community were surprised to discover that their hospital was also to be included in the TSA's plans. They thought, not unreasonably, that this went well beyond any acceptable remit since Lewisham Hospital had no organisational connection with the trust to which the administrator had been appointed and was in the entirely separate Lewisham Healthcare NHS Trust.

Over the next few months the TSA prepared his draft report. As it became clear that Lewisham Hospital would figure large in the proposals, members of the Lewisham community, the hospital health staff, patient groups and GPs came together to create a campaign group to oppose the recommendations – the Save Lewisham Hospital Campaign. The group also had the support of the mayor of Lewisham, the borough council and the three Lewisham MPs, all Labour.

The TSA's draft report was published on 29 October 2012 and a period of thirty working days was allowed for consultation beginning on 2 November. The report's recommendations would have had a dramatic impact on Lewisham Hospital, ending its major hospital status and removing all acute and maternity services provision from the local community. The administrator recommended, in addition to several proposals affecting the South London Health Trust, that Lewisham Hospital's newly refurbished A&E (costing £12 million), all acute adult and children's admitting wards, adult critical care, emergency and complex surgery units should be closed and maternity services closed or severely curtailed. He also proposed the sell-off of 60 per cent of Lewisham Hospital's buildings estate, which would be released by the closures, and that Lewisham Hospital should become a south-east London centre for elective surgery.

The response from the Lewisham community was highly significant. Here was a group of people who were not going to meekly accept the administrator's solution. They decided to fight the proposals in the full knowledge that in doing so they would have to master the details and the financial implications of a complex package. But they sensed, correctly, that behind the jargon was a brutal assault on much of what the NHS meant to them.

More than 6,000 people, including more than 4,000 Lewisham residents, responded in written form to the draft report, including an online questionnaire, created for the administrator by the polling company Ipsos MORI.[53] In response to the question about changes to the Lewisham A&E department, 90 per cent were 'strongly opposed' while among Lewisham residents the level of opposition rose to 96 per cent.[54] Hundreds of residents

---

53 Ipsos MORI Independent Consultation Feedback Report, Table A3, p. 94: Appendix I. TSA Final Report Securing Sustainable NHS Services, 7 January 2013.
54 Ibid., pp. 37, 42.

attended the three consultation meetings with the administrator and his panel at different venues in the borough. A petition started by Heidi Alexander, the MP for Lewisham East, was handed in to 10 Downing Street in December and to the Department of Health on 30 January 2013, by which time there were 51,854 signatures in opposition to the proposals. More than 400 GPs opposed the report, including over 90 per cent of Lewisham GPs. A large demonstration involving 15,000 local people took place on 26 November 2012 and the formal consultation finished on 13 December 2012.

On 26 January 2013 a second demonstration took place, this time with 25,000 people, including our family. At the finishing point a rally was held. The mood had to be experienced to be believed. There was no forced exuberance, but a quiet confidence that right would triumph. The entire Owen family of eleven people comprising three generations felt deeply indebted to Lewisham Hospital. Just like hundreds of thousands of other people we deeply resented that the voices of the local community and clinicians had not been taken into account. My daughter-in-law, herself a doctor of medicine with a PhD in brain imaging and in training to be a child psychiatrist at the Maudsley, had given birth to both her daughters at the hospital, which was in walking distance of their home. My daughter's two children had been delivered there. The second child was originally scheduled to be a home birth but on the advice of the midwife she had been quickly transferred to the hospital by ambulance.

Five days after the march, on 31 January 2013, we knew our fate. The Secretary of State announced his devastating decision:

1. that Lewisham Hospital be downgraded from major hospital status;

2. that Lewisham's A&E, all acute admitting wards including the children's wards, intensive care and all emergency and complex surgery be closed;

3. that 60 per cent of the Lewisham Hospital estate be sold off;

4. that a 'small but safe' A&E – a non-admitting service with 24/7 senior emergency medical cover – be established;

5. that a small midwifeled birth unit without obstetric medical or emergency back-up be established; and

6. that a walk-in paediatric urgent care service be established.

This represented little change from the TSA's original proposals – except for the 'small but safe' A&E, the midwife-led birth unit and the walk-in paediatric urgent care service. None of these had formed part of the consultation. The arguments of the Secretary of State, Jeremy Hunt, who had succeeded Andrew Lansley, for accepting the recommendations – namely that the South London Healthcare NHS Trust was 'the most financially challenged in the country' and 'only by looking beyond the boundaries of the Trust' could a 'viable solution' be found – exposed the weaknesses and the mistakes inherent in the 2012 legislation and can be found in the Hansard record of the House of Commons for that day.

NHS guidance states that four 'threshold tests' should be met for major health service reconfigurations:

1. Support from GP commissioners (local clinical commissioning groups or CCGs).
2. Clarity on the clinical evidence base for improvement.
3. Strengthened public and patient engagement in the consultation process.
4. Consistency with current and prospective patient choice, i.e. justification for any restriction of choice.

The Secretary of State asserted that these had all been met in the case of Lewisham. The challenge facing the people of Lewisham was to demonstrate that the Secretary of State was wrong and in doing so demonstrate that even if Parliament was ineffective the people could still appeal to the law of the land through judicial review.

Following Hunt's announcement it became apparent to hospital clinicians, Lewisham GPs, the community, patients and politicians in Lewisham, that as well as a mass of evidence and opinion having been ignored, the validity of the evidence cited was highly questionable, particularly that '100 lives would be saved'. A decision was therefore taken to seek a judicial review. The judicial review procedure was of great importance and it was led by the Save Lewisham Hospital Campaign but also hugely helped by Lewisham Borough Council, not just supporting but putting its financial resources behind searches through the masses of documents available under the disclosure proceedings. The review procedure would probably not have been successful without this documentary search and the material it revealed. It was a dramatic way of demonstrating that health in its widest sense is not just the responsibility of hospital trusts or even general practitioners but of the whole community.

Many protests take place over hospital closures. What was unusual in this case was the desire among the protestors for natural justice and for those who had given evidence to the TSA to 'have their day in court'. The Save Lewisham Hospital Campaign, in addition to supporting judicial review, decided to carry out what the government had signally failed to do: to establish an inquiry that would actually pay attention to the evidence, so that the voices of those who had been ignored could resonate within Lewisham and beyond.

The campaign revived the concept of a people's commission, which has a recognised history and an established precedent, though not so much in the UK as elsewhere. Bertrand Russell convened a tribunal of international civic conscience on Vietnam in 1966, which was reconvened to examine the issue of Palestine in 2010–12. In both cases there was felt to be a need to highlight un-redressed violations of international law, by the USA in the first instance and Israel in the second. Another somewhat similar tribunal took place in The Hague to focus on human rights abuse in Iran. These initiatives had been motivated and organised by civil society but the Lewisham initiative was truly groundbreaking in taking on a domestic issue.

The terms of reference were extremely important. The commission did not come into existence just to conduct a public debate. It attempted to conduct a quasi-judicial process. The powers and resources that a judicial inquiry would have at its disposal did not of course apply, but, nevertheless, the proceedings of the commission were designed to highlight the issues that the government and the administrator had studiously ignored.

I was asked to speak and so I found myself with my wife, a

son and a granddaughter sitting in Broadway Theatre, Catford on the morning of 29 June with a paper cup of coffee in my hand listening to Elizabeth Woodcraft, a barrister at Tooks Chambers, explaining the procedure. A panel of four barristers would do the questioning. A panel of three assessors would reach conclusions. The first assessor was Blake Morrison, a writer and journalist whose book *And When Did You Last See Your Father?* I had read with delight and for which he won an important award. He had also written a study of the James Bulger murder, *As If.* He had been a literary editor of *The Observer* and the *Independent on Sunday* before becoming a full-time writer. Aptly for the purpose of the inquiry he was now Professor of Creative and Life Writing at Goldsmiths College, only a few miles down the road from the meeting place. He lived in south-east London and knew Lewisham Hospital very well.

The second panellist was Baroness Warnock, a fellow member of the House of Lords and a crossbench life peer. A moral philosopher of great distinction, she had shaped government policy on many issues. In 1974 she chaired an inquiry on special education, which brought about radical change by placing emphasis on the teaching and learning of disabled children in mainstream schools. From 1979 to 1984 she sat on the Royal Commission on environmental pollution and from 1982 to 1984 she chaired the committee of inquiry into human fertilisation, which gave rise to the Human Fertilisation and Embryology Act 1990, which led in turn, among other things, to the development of policy on IVF treatment. It was hard to think of anyone better qualified to assess the issues impartially and it was a wonderful endorsement of the very idea behind the commission that she had agreed to attend.

The chair of the panel was Michael Mansfield QC, who had represented defendants in criminal trials, appeals and inquiries in some of the most controversial legal cases in Britain. He represented the family of Jean Charles de Menezes, killed by police at a London Underground station in 2005, and the families of victims at the Bloody Sunday inquiry. He chaired an inquiry into the shoot-to-kill policy in Northern Ireland and had represented many families at inquests, including those into the *Marchioness* disaster, the Deptford/New Cross fire and the Lockerbie bombings. At the time of our inquiry he was representing the family of Stephen Lawrence.

Everyone taking part had given up much of their time in preparing for the day, and offered their work and attendance for free. Many witnesses who wanted to give evidence to the inquiry had made statements, but not all the statements could be heard within a single day. The strategy was to concentrate the evidence and call live witnesses to give the main features of the deep concerns that had given rise to the inquiry.

There were several witnesses, including Jeremy Hunt and his adviser, Sir Bruce Keogh, who had been invited but were not present. Their words, spoken or written in Parliament or in letters, were read by an actor, Tim Preece. The proceedings were all recorded on video.[55]

Mansfield introduced the concept:

A people's commission or tribunal: it is not a novel concept. In fact historically you can trace its origins back to the English

---

55 Video available at http://www.savelewishamhospital.com/lewisham-peoples-commission-of-inquiry-2/ (accessed 21 November 2014).

Civil War – the Levellers, the Diggers and everything that went on at St Mary's Church, Putney. So if you want to go back that far, you can find out that there is a tradition that is extremely important. But it comes into its own just after the Second World War in an entirely different way which has led to this one. There was a situation where you had the Universal Declaration of Human Rights in 1948 and then you had the Charter for the United Nations, and what Bertrand Russell discovered in the wake of those was that actually they were not being implemented; actually they were not being respected. So what he did was to set up the first international people's tribunal.

I have been sitting on one of the successors to that, but *he* did it in relation to Vietnam and American violations of international law in Vietnam. I have been doing it in relation to Israeli violations of war in relation to Palestine. The importance of them was this: that it was world citizenry saying 'We want something done, we want the violations highlighted'. But of course highlighting is not enough, you need action, and that is what it started, and it made a difference. And since then there have been a whole series of them. In fact there is a permanent people's tribunal set up in Bologna looking at international issues.

But internally there have been similar things to this over the past two decades and do not believe for one moment, despite government dismissal, or pretending to ignore what is going on, that they actually do not recognise what is happening. They are not here because they cannot face the music. And I think for a people's tribunal we face this many, many times over. That the people who are given the opportunity when criticised in the proper way of natural justice actually do not turn up. So, it's a real arrogance – which of course is the thing we are examining in relation to policy.'

Mansfield went on to explain that the commission would examine two things, and the first would be broken into two parts:

Firstly the original vision and principles underpinning the NHS, with particular reference to the community it serves and its accountability to that community. The second part to the first point: the extent to which the vision and principles have been eroded by the imposition of the internal market and recent moves to open the NHS to external market forces; and the degree to which these changes have been openly debated.

Secondly the extent to which this process has culminated in the potential destruction of quality healthcare for the community of Lewisham and south-east London, exemplified by the proposals for Lewisham Hospital. . . . The plan in fact is effectively the sell-off of 60 per cent of the Lewisham Hospital estate.

Mansfield drew attention to the International Covenant on Economic, Political and Cultural Rights.

This covenant is extremely important because it was brought about in 1966; the United Kingdom signed it in 1968 and they ratified it in 1978 – Article 12. It is important to have these sorts of texts because if we as a panel are going to be challenged or anyone else is going to be challenged about the fundamental basis or existence of something like this exercise, Article 12 behoves those who signed and ratified – including the United Kingdom – to create conditions to ensure healthcare for all, a very simple proposition, and there are four 'A's that are attached to that. In other words, if it is going to be ensuring access to healthcare for all, it has got to be *available*; it has got to be *accessible*; it has got to be *affordable*; and it has got to be *acceptable*. Those are the four 'A's – they are not the same as the four criteria that were set down by the government for their proposals for Lewisham and south-east London [cited above].

He went on to explain that the following week there was to be a judicial review where the High Court was going to examine the legality of the decision and whether it was *ultra vires* or *intra vires*. It would also look at the four criteria set down by the government.

The concerns with the decision made by the Secretary of State were expressed in graphic terms by the campaign spokeswoman, Simone Boothe, who spoke first:

We have no intention of stopping; no matter how tired we are, no matter what other direction we are being pulled in, we will be here until the bitter end. If Jeremy Hunt – not that I'm wishing any ill harm to him at all – but if he happened to have an accident in Lewisham, I'm sure he'd hope that there would be an A&E there, possibly not a maternity, as he is a gentleman, but I am hoping that he would hope there would be an A&E there to serve him, just like we want an A&E there to serve us.'

The Mayor of Lewisham, Sir Steve Bullock, said:

Lewisham Hospital is a key part of the fabric of public service provision in Lewisham. Its long history in the borough stretches back before the creation of the NHS to the emergence of Poor Law provisions in south-east London. Over the past fifteen years Lewisham Hospital has established itself as a highly effective district general hospital in both clinical and financial terms, serving a local population of some 300,000 people and with an annual turnover of £240 million. In 2010 the hospital was commissioned to provide community health services. This has allowed for the vertical integration of acute and community services and has provided stronger links to the council services and other primary care services.

The hospital's links within the health economy of south-east London are positive and strong. Its work with the council's adult care system is highly effective. It has also played a key role in contributing to Lewisham's collective achievement of an outstanding rating for children's safeguarding. The strength of clinical and public sentiment evident since the proposals were published reflects the professional and public esteem in which the institution is held, not only for the quality of its healthcare provision, but also its role and place in the local community. In addition to the services it provides, Lewisham Hospital is a well-regarded public institution contributing to the fabric of civic life and a key element of people's sense of place and wellbeing. The hospital is a major local employer and acts as a hub for volunteering and community activities. There are many points that the council has made in its public statements that the commission could consider, but I wish to draw a few particularly to your attention.

The basis of our judicial review is that the trust special administrator's powers extend only to making recommendations about the future of the NHS trust to which they were appointed, in this instance the South London Healthcare NHS Trust. It is our view that the TSA did not have the power to make recommendations which would affect Lewisham Healthcare NHS Trust, nor did the Secretary of State in response to any such recommendation have the power to accept them. Supported by independent analysis, the council believe that the problem has not been framed correctly. The regime for unsustainable providers was designed to remedy failing hospitals. It was not designed to establish in fine detail the healthcare needs of a given population. It is acknowledged that changes are required for acute healthcare to be organised effectively in south-east London. However, such changes need to start with the needs of the population of south-east London and not the financial and productivity needs of the healthcare providers. Throughout his draft report the TSA adopted a strict provider focus and failed to take into account or assess any impact of his recommendations on the local population or the extent to which these changes destabilised other local systems and processes.

The Council also considers that the options analysis

undertaken by the TSA in respect of the hospitals concerned was unbalanced and that the method for evaluating and weighting the criteria selected by the TSA was flawed. We consider that the TSA failed to recognise the cost-effectiveness of local partnership arrangements. These are designed to reduce unnecessary hospital admission and develop community-based provision. In the council's view, these cannot be replicated across four hospital sites without affecting the quality of provision and incurring additional costs for both health and social care commissioners.

In relation to maternity, children's and older people's services the council considers that the TSA has failed to address the impact on patient and carer family choice and the need as far as possible for care to be delivered close to home.

Finally, the council is concerned that, despite the failure of the South London Healthcare Trust, which merged three hospitals in 2009, the TSA proposal is to demerge and then remerge hospitals without regard to the reasons for the failure of South London Healthcare Trust, nor any apparent consideration of the risks associated with such new mergers. As both a former chair of Lewisham Hospital itself and as the borough's mayor, I am clear that, were these current proposals to go ahead, the residents of this part of London would find the healthcare available to them significantly damaged.

I was then asked to talk about the wider implications for the NHS. I was deeply affected by what I had just heard and spoke spontaneously and from the heart.

I was ten years old in 1948 when the NHS started. My father was a GP in Plymouth, my mother was a dentist and that day was a day which my father called 'a day of freedom'. It was the day he no longer had to ask patients to pay for coming to see him with their illnesses. He remembered the twenties and the thirties, the fragmented healthcare service, voluntary hospitals, hospitals run by local authorities, private hospitals: a healthcare system which was not matching the needs of the people. Sadly too many people forget those days. . . .

When we look back we must also look forward. Here we are: the NHS – with all the adverse reports that we have been reading in the newspapers and the things that have gone wrong – remains the most popular public service in the whole country. Not only is it popular in this country, it is admired across the world and its record of achievement of cost-effective care is remarkable. We pay a lot less than most countries in a sophisticated world of healthcare and we get a better service.

It is extraordinary really when you look back to this achievement, the greatest social achievement in my view in post war Britain, and here we are in 2013 looking at a situation where the NHS will, unless something changes within the next few years, be completely and totally changed – changed out of all recognition. Don't forget that! This legislation that came in in 2012 – 457 pages' worth, 309 clauses, larger than Nye Bevan's original NHS legislation – is a serious sustained attack on the very principles and ethics of the National Health Service.

My wife is American. She came here forty-three years

ago. She blesses the National Health Service. We, like most families, have had some serious illnesses. I am here in part because my three children all live in south London and use this hospital. We went on the march, my wife and I, with two of our grandchildren, both of whom had used the hospital.

But this is not a NIMBY issue, this is not against closures of any hospital. I trained as a doctor at St Thomas' Hospital, I did my midwifery training at the Lambeth Hospital: now closed and thankfully closed. My first job was in the Royal Waterloo Hospital: closed because of new provisions. I am not against the fact that hospitals have to close, that there has to be reconfiguring, but I am very against the proposals that are being put forward in this way and as they affect Lewisham Hospital. It is not for me to make here the judgements about this, but I do want to draw attention to an extremely important report that has just literally come out – it is not even finally completed. This is the first objective study of what is being done, or being attempted to be done, here in south London and it is an academic, not a political, document. You will later hear from Professor Allyson Pollock of the Public Health Research and Policy Department at Queen Mary, University of London.

What this shows is that what we are discussing here and what is being evaluated by this commission has a direct relevance to the National Health Service's future. Are we going to just accept the marketisation of the Health Service? Are we just going to accept that the Health Service can be taken from us? Just remember this: no Conservative Prime Minister – Winston Churchill right through to John Major

– has wanted to change the Health Service. The one that did, Margaret Thatcher, looked at the issue and found it politically too toxic to make the changes. It was only in 2010, after an election in which we were promised by the now Prime Minister, David Cameron, that there would not be another top down reorganisation, that we have been faced by this legislation. With no democratic mandate whatever, the Conservatives and Liberal Democrats are trying to take away a statutory, legal obligation of the Secretary of State for Health to provide a comprehensive healthcare system.

These are fundamental and important changes, but they have repercussions. Those changes are being seen here in south London and what you are trying to assess today, and what the judicial review will start looking at on Tuesday, has profound implications for what will happen to the NHS up and down the country. We have already seen one judicial review in Leeds, mainly about paediatric cardiology, and what we did find was that the review threw out the government's proposals because their facts were wrong. This study [by Allyson Pollock] shows that many of the supposed 'facts' are fundamentally flawed and wrong, and the interpretation and the way that this has been done, if it goes through here in Lewisham, will have profound implications elsewhere. So I hope that the commission will find some way of getting this document before the judicial review on Tuesday, very difficult and very late to be able to do it, but there is a provision for friends of the court, but it is up to you.

I say to you today, what you are doing here is protecting your own hospital, as you have every right as individuals to do, but you are not pursuing just the normal objection to any hospital closure, you are actually pioneering a people's challenge to the fundamental politics that underlie it. It is being greatly changed by this private finance initiative [PFI]; in my view, it is a political fix, as is really this overall government policy which is affecting the issues of your hospital. Good luck to you and I hope you succeed.

The reference to PFI in my speech is crucial because of its central impact on the whole of the Lewisham Hospital controversy and therefore the record of the interview between Professor Allyson Pollock, now the chair of the Campaign for the NHS Reinstatement Bill 2015, and the barrister Nicola Braganza in the commission proceedings is very important. A more eloquent explanation of PFI is hard to find. The issue of PFI is taken up in the last chapter of this book with the innovative suggestion of creating a charitable NHS Investment Fund to relieve the NHS of PFI repayments.

NICOLA BRAGANZA: Professor Pollock, could you give first of all an outline of your expertise?

ALLYSON POLLOCK: I am a Professor of Public Health Policy and Research at Queen Mary, University of London. I trained in medicine and then I trained in public health and so for the last twenty years as part of my work I've been looking at the effect and impact of privatisation on the NHS and government policies, and one big area of work has been looking at public–private partnerships as they are called, or the effect of the Private Finance Initiative across the public sector, but particularly in healthcare.

NB: I would like to ask you first about private finance initiatives and in particular a report that you've prepared, *PFI and the National Health Service in England*, together with David Price, senior research fellow, and that is dated June this year. In particular the report sets out that by April 2009 101 of the 133 new hospitals built between 1997 and 2008 or under construction were privately financed and it sets out that by April 2011 across the public sector more than 700 PFI contracts have been signed in the UK with an estimated capital value of almost £50 billion in England alone and annual repayments estimated at £8 billion for thirty to sixty years. What is the consequence of that? How has PFI featured in large NHS projects?

AP: PFI: instead of the government doing the borrowing or using taxes – and governments can borrow very, very cheaply indeed – they go to the private sector and they ask the private sector to do the borrowing. So they are borrowing through banks and service operators and equity investors. And the whole problem of going down that route is that it is very, very expensive, so the cost of private finance is incredibly expensive.

So the government borrows the money, but the problem is that the hospital trusts are left with the debt and these are thirty-year contracts – and it is often extended to sixty-year contracts. So the hospitals have to service the debts from their operating budgets. This is a very expensive way of borrowing money. Research by Jim and Margaret Cuthbert has shown that for every single hospital designed and built and that is operating for the next thirty years, we are actually paying for two, but we are only getting one – and in some cases we are paying for three. So, if you can imagine two or three: St Bartholomew's Hospital in central London is my hospital: it's a PFI trust – we could have had three of those! But actually at the moment we are only getting one, so that tells you how expensive it is and how lucrative these deals are for bankers and the investors.

NB: That brings me to the next point, which is: what is the accountability in the PFI contracts?

AP: One of the big problems with PFI is that the contracts are commercial and often they are commercial in confidence, and neither the government nor the commercial contractors have an interest in revealing these contracts to the public, so they remain secret, and even Parliament and the select committees have had extreme difficulty trying to get an understanding of how much exactly we are paying. So we don't know quite how much interest we're paying and what the returns are to the investors and all the other beneficiaries. So, they are commercial, in confidence, and they have not been open to public scrutiny.

NB: Following on from that, in your report you refer to the fraudulent manipulation. What do you mean about that?

AP: Well, one of the ironies is that some of the banks that we bailed out in 2010 – like the Royal Bank of Scotland, where we poured in billions of pounds, so these banks in theory we own – are actually rebuilding their balance sheets on the back of PFI, because they are still continuing to charge the public sector hundreds of millions of pounds in excess interest charges. And many of these banks also have equity stakes, so they are making extraordinary returns on their investment. The chair of the Public Accounts Committee, who is a Conservative, called it 'the unacceptable face of capitalism', so high are these returns.

So, this is a really significant issue that the banks have been investing heavily. They are rebuilding their balance sheets, but they were also implicated in some of the fraudulent manipulation of the interest rates. So, if you think about it now, interest rates are about 0.5 per cent. So government borrowing would be about 1.5–2 per cent. And now on these PFI schemes we can be paying anything from 6 per cent to 15 per cent. That's just on the interest and of course there is a real issue as to whether the banks were actually manipulating and fixing the interest rates in the run-up to signing of some of these PFI deals; and these are questions that remain there and have to be answered.

NB: Thank you. I want to now move on and ask you about the TSA report and the analysis that you've just completed, and that's entitled *The TSA Regime and the South London Healthcare NHS Trust: A Case of Blaming the Victims.*[56] . . . As a result of your analysis, what have you found to be the main consequences of that report?

AP: Originally I had started off just looking at the national PFIs, but in the last couple of weeks it became very evident to me there was a bigger story going on in south London. What our report really shows is the way in which the problems of south London are being driven by central government policies, which include the Private Finance Initiative. So the

---

56 The report's final title was *Blaming the Victims: The Trust Special Administrator's Plans for South East London*. It is available at http://www.allysonpollock.com/wp-content/uploads/2013/07/AP_2013_Pollock_BlamingTheVictim.pdf (accessed 4 November 2014).

government has landed South London Healthcare Trust, which included Greenwich and Bromley, with enormous debts, an unaffordable situation that they can't get out of.

On the way here the taxi driver said, 'The problem for Lewisham is that it is going to close, but it is the other hospitals in the area that messed it up.' That is not true. It is not the other hospitals that have messed it up: it's government policies that have messed it up. What the TSA has done is decide to try and resolve the issues locally, when these are national issues. It is not a local issue. So, the national policies include the use of private finance, which is making the whole system unaffordable locally, because South London Healthcare Trust has not one, but six PFI schemes, so if I tell you that for every hospital that is built, you could have had two or three running – that's what you're paying for – you begin to see the scale of the problem.

The second problem is that other government policies include a deliberate policy of underfunding trusts, so trust incomes are falling while the PFI charges are rising. And PFI is very, very hungry, because not only are we paying very high rates of interest, the PFI charge is indexed to the measure of inflation, so the budgets for the NHS are falling, but the PFI charge is rising by about 4 or 5 per cent a year. If I just give you an illustration, at the Princess Royal University Hospital in Bromley, the PFI payment has risen to £39 million a year and by the contract's close in 2030 – the contracts have been extended – it is £94 million. The PFIs just now are taking between 18 and 20 per cent of the trust's income.

That's a lot of money because before, PFI hospitals

paid nothing from their income for capital and then the government brought in something called a capital charge, which meant they were paying around 4 per cent of their income. So, there is a big difference between nonPFI hospitals, which are paying 4–6 per cent of their income, and PFI hospitals, which are paying out to the bankers and shareholders anything from 15 to 30 per cent of their income.

If you remember a hospital's income mainly is spent on the staff – and staff are vital for the quality of care, as you all know – so, if you're paying the PFI and your bankers and your service operators and investors, you've less money to pay for staff, so something has to go.

NB: What has the TSA failed to do?

AP: The TSA plans are more major service reductions and budget cuts. The TSA's report has focused almost completely on the financial situation, but it failed to give the proper analysis. It has absolutely failed in that respect because it has made this a local problem that can only be solved by closing 15 per cent of the beds across London. That includes beds at Guy's and 41 per cent of the beds at Lewisham.

What it absolutely failed to do – and this is totally irresponsible – normally when you have a major service closure, a reconfiguration, you would do a needs assessment, you would say 'All right, we're going to change our services. Where will these patients go and how will services be re-provided?' The TSA failed to do that and what we actually show is that there are no significant serious planning details or planning data in the TSA report or indeed in any of the expensive management consultant reports they've commissioned. So they commissioned Deloitte to do the MORI opinion poll, but that's not a measure of access or need; and they commissioned very expensive management consultants to look at travel times and travel access. Travel times are important, but actually the really important thing is: what are the public's needs and how are they going to be met and where are they going to be met and how are services going to be staffed?

Because what we do know from the TSA report is that we are going to see major service closures and major reductions in the staffing budgets, and that doesn't just include Lewisham, that also includes all of the neighbouring trusts, who are going to have to reduce their staff. So, where are patients going to go, how are they going to be treated and who is going to treat them? And the one thing we know from the Francis report in Mid Staffs was that the focus on financial targets was to the detriment of patient care. The managers put the financial targets before they put the needs of the patients and that meant they cut the services, they cut the staff and there was no good quality of care. We now have lots of Mid Staffs in the making here, not just in south-east London, but across the country.

NB: Thank you. Finally, your recommendations as a result of your analysis: what are the key recommendations that you make?

AP: I am going to read them out, because I think they are quite important. We found that the TSA report is not evidence based, its financial analysis is poor and misjudged and they have not conducted a proper needs assessment or planning. Because of that, we recommend:

1. That the TSA regime for the South London Hospital Trust should be revoked and the case should be reconsidered afresh, excluding the effect of government policies.

2. If it's the case that such reconsideration leads to rejigging of the regime, then our second recommendation is that the TSA recommendations should only occur when a proper needs assessment has been done and when all the data, including the PFI contracts, are placed in the public domain.

3. With a third recommendation that the government should make public and renegotiate all the NHS PFI contracts, the six South London Healthcare Trust's and the King's Trust's as well; and, in default of which, Parliament should act to require the government to do so in order that Parliament, and we the public, can better understand the reasons for the high cost of finance; can take steps to control those costs; and can have confidence in the credibility and fairness of government decisions made on the basis of them.

4. Our fourth recommendation is that the TSA regime should not in the future be applied to trusts whose deficits have been significantly contributed to by government policies, as is the case here in south-east London.

5. Finally, the TSA regime in future should not be permitted without a proper needs assessment. It should not be permitted to use productivity measures and targets as a substitute for planning and access. It should not be permitted to use travel times as proxy measure of public's use and need for services. It should not use

MORI opinion polls as a substitute for public health planning and it should not use data that has not been put in the public domain. (*Applause*)

Michael Mansfield then asked Pollock a question:

MICHAEL MANSFIELD: When one talks about the financial markets and when one talks about the initiative that you have, and that really the responsibility is not the hospitals', but in fact the government policy in regard to this, and then you need to assess the needs of a community, has there been any quantification of the needs? In other words, if they go ahead with these proposals, what are the social and economic factors that have really not been quantified? In other words, it is no saving at all or am I wrong?

AP: We know that from other hospital closures that there have been really no savings at all that have happened. So we have got past evidence of that so you can cut services, cut staff and there are no savings. But you are talking also about indirect costs: so – unemployment, people being sick, not getting back to work, not having their operations and there has been no quantification of that impact, neither in previous hospital downsizing and service closures or in this. And I should say that PFI is a bit of an engine for service closures because every PFI hospital scheme when it opens has affordability problems and it's necessitated going from three hospitals into one, but there has been nothing on the indirect costs and that has never been quantified or analysed at any point.

MM: Is there anybody doing it at the moment?

AP: Not to my knowledge, but I am sure you could find some management consultants to do it for many millions of pounds.

An audience of 400 people, formed mainly of Lewisham residents but also including those who had travelled from further afield, listened over the course of the day to the commission hearing.[57]

Michael Mansfield summed up:

We need to ensure that the public at large, well beyond the boundaries of Lewisham, recognise what is going on. It's going on in all the welfare services of course, what is going on with their National Health, and we don't want them suddenly to wake up – which at the moment they may do if they're not careful – to find that what they depended on since 1948 has disappeared. Now I just want to say this about 1948. We will bear in mind what I've talked about, the United Nations Declaration of Human Rights and the right to health. But in 1948, a letter went through everybody's letter boxes, and the letter said this about the inauguration of the National Health Service: 'It will provide you all with medical, dental and nursing care. Everyone, rich or poor, man, woman or child, can use it or any part of it. There are no charges, except for a few special items. There are no insurance qualifications.

---

57 Witness statements from both live witnesses and those giving written evidence can be found separately online at http://www.savelewishamhospital.com/commission-witnesses_. During the hearing it became clear that further documents were relevant and these have been provided by the relevant witnesses. They appear online at http://www.savelewishamhospital.com/commission-witnesses alongside the statements of the relevant witnesses.

It's not a charity, you're paying for it through tax. But it will relieve your money worries in times of illness.' So in a sense that was the gold standard that was set in 1948 alongside the Declaration of Human Rights. None of this should be forgotten. And none of it should be forgotten in the context of what had happened in the Second World War. You were dealing with the ashes and embers of a nation that had been battered, a nation that had had its industry knocked out. But an industry that stood together, in one sense, within those ashes, the phoenix was arising. It shows what is possible, whatever the economic exigencies.

And so we're very conscious of the background when we come to consider everything that has happened today.

Michael Mansfield concluded his summary by saying:

'Finally what is the basis, what is the evidence basis? As a lawyer I'm always concerned to see what is the evidence. Not what is the speculation but what the evidence is. If you're going to have far-reaching reconfiguration, which sometimes takes up to ten years, you've got to do it properly. Which means not only consultation but you actually have to know what the impact is going to be. And you don't know the impact until you've discovered what it is you're serving. What is the community? What are their needs? Well, it's perfectly clear from today, and also from the written material we have, this is an area that we'll examine very, very closely, because it so far appears: there was absolutely no evidential basis and the basis that they did come up with – the 100 saved lives – nobody knows where they got it from.

Professor Colin Leys, a retired professor of politics now attached to Goldsmiths, University of London (located, as it happens, in the Borough of Lewisham), for the last decade had focused on the development of health policy and the NHS. He made the following points to the panel about the 2012 legislation:

> To my mind the most [recent] fundamental change is that it replaces patient need as the top priority with the need to meet commercial targets, the need to balance the books, the need to stay solvent. At lot of people think 'Well, what's new about that, because haven't they always had to be careful about money?' and of course the NHS was always short of money, so doctors were never free to do whatever they thought the patients absolutely needed. But what is new is the shift in the order. Before, you thought 'What do patients need and what can we do with the money we've got?' Now you think 'What must we do to balance the books this year, to balance the competition?' And think about patients separately. And we have already seen the consequences of that at Mid-Stafford and in other places.

While the points raised by Professor Leys affect all NHS trusts and all sectors of the NHS, the panel felt that they provided a useful background for understanding how financial pressures rather than patient care formed the background to the work and interventions of the TSA in south London and Lewisham.

Leys also drew the panel's attention to the increasing proportion of the NHS budget being swallowed up simply 'by the need to operate a market' (10 per cent at a conservative estimate) on top of other management costs. This is a factor, he stated, that is never discussed. Furthermore, he highlighted for us a significant change in accountability. The Secretary of State is now only responsible for 'promoting' the Health Service in England and the people actually responsible for operating it are NHS England and Monitor. (He was speaking here specifically about England and not Scotland, Wales or Northern Ireland.) NHS England is 'a bureaucratic branch in effect of the Department of Health, but is a body appointed by the Secretary of State, but is not accountable to the Secretary of State.'

The actor Tim Preece read the words of the Secretary of State concerning the basis of the decisions: 'These proposals, as amended, could save up to 100 lives every year through higher clinical standards.' John O'Donohue, consultant physician at Lewisham Hospital, told the panel:

We did challenge the Secretary of State and Professor Sir Bruce Keogh on this figure and I am disappointed to say that the response from Bruce Keogh contained the phrase 'This is not an exact science'. If you go into the basis for this it all hangs on research from nearly ten years ago, from 2004. And this research looked at emergency admissions in England over a period of one year and they found patients coming in at the weekend had a mortality that was higher than patients who were admitted during the week; and they made the heroic claim from that evidence that this meant that patients weren't properly being looked after over the weekend and, therefore, they were more likely to die as a result of that.

If you go into the actual academic paper, the authors

themselves actually concede that there is another potential explanation for this. When they looked at the patients admitted at the weekend, in any 24-hour period at the weekend only three-quarters of the numbers of patients were admitted compared to the weekdays. These patients admitted at the weekend were sicker to start with.

This phenomenon arose, O'Donohue explained, because most people avoid going to the doctor or attending hospital at the weekend. If they can they will 'tough it out' until Monday. So those that feel they must go to A&E are inevitably those who are more unwell. He said:

Just to expand on that, I'll take an extreme example: patients admitted on Christmas Day. Christmas Day is a day nobody wants to end up spending in A&E. We know that patients admitted on Christmas Day are of a higher mortality because they are sicker to start with and this is what we are seeing in this paper and this is the basis of the whole premise that '100 lives will be saved'.

He then described how the figure was arrived at:

What the paper showed was that the excess mortality at the weekends was 3,300 for England and they broke this down on the back of an envelope and calculated that for the south-east of London pro rata this would be 100 lives and this is the basis for the whole clinical justification that the Secretary of State has made.

O'Donohue also referred to other, chilling, information which had come to light since the Secretary of State's decision:

> We have had Sir Bruce Keogh's other predictions of mortality since then in the Leeds cardiothoracic case. [Data, later shown to be invalid, had formed the basis for an emergency decision by Keogh to suspend children's heart surgery at Leeds General Infirmary in March 2013, to the distress of parents and potential damage to patient care.] I think that can only serve to undermine his role in this.

On the effect of department closures, he said they had 'had direct experience of the closure of an A&E department in England. A Freedom of Information request for Newark A&E showed that the death rate for patients living in Newark who had to be shipped to a neighbouring A&E when Newark A&E closed rose by 25 per cent.' The Secretary of State had proposed that Lewisham should retain a 'small but safe' A&E department, but the opinion of Dr Chidi Ejimofo, consultant in emergency medicine at Lewisham Hospital, was that there is no such thing. If the proposals were to go through, the panel heard, Lewisham would lose four of the seven essential services needed to support an A&E department: paediatrics, acute medicine, surgery and intensive care. In Ejimofo's view, without these essential services the so-called A&E department would be no more than an urgent care centre.

O'Donohue also assisted us with the Secretary of State's assertion that services should be centralised to save lives. We noted particularly the dates in his explanation of the treatment accorded to stroke and heart attack patients. He said:

We do know that for some conditions centralised care is better and that's why since 2011 all patients with strokes have been centralised; they haven't been coming to Lewisham, they have been [going] to King's [College Hospital, Camberwell] or to Princess Royal in Farnborough [near Orpington]. Since 2009 all heart attacks have been diverted, either from A&E in Lewisham or by the London Ambulance Service, to specialised heart attack centres and we know the centralisation of these has resulted in a better mortality for stroke and heart attack. *But they are the only situations where this applies* [panel's emphasis].

In other words, *these changes were already in place* before the Secretary of State's proposals came into being.

O'Donohue made a distinction between the centralised and thus improved care for stroke and heart patients, and other conditions where speed is also of the essence in terms of treatment:

An example of that is meningitis, where it has been shown that what is important for meningitis is the speed you get antibiotics into the patient, not where it is delivered. And so the Secretary of State made a very surprising claim in his speech when he announced in his decision that meningitis patients would benefit [from centralised care]. That is completely contradicted by the specialist societies and the evidence.

Dr Donal O'Sullivan, consultant in public health medicine for the London Borough of Lewisham, described his 'grave concerns about the TSA's proposals'. In relation to the question of what would be required to deliver safe and effective services for children and pregnant women in Lewisham, O'Sullivan pointed to evidence of overstretched maternity resources in the south-east area overall. 'My main concern is essentially about capacity generally. Within the sector at present we are constantly on the bones of not having enough beds, in not having enough capacity to deliver a safe service. That's in the whole sector.'

He described research carried out over a period of eighteen months, looking at all the trusts in south-east London, which showed that 'on average each month, at least two of those units had to close on at least one occasion; and that's almost always because of beds, because of a lack of capacity. . . . I think we're on the brink of a major problem with capacity in maternity services in south-east London.'

O'Sullivan was concerned about the assumptions of the TSA that women would go to one specific alternative hospital if they could not go to Lewisham Hospital to give birth:

> The proposals clearly assume that most of the flow will go to Greenwich. There's no evidence for that that I can see. Women in Lewisham historically, if they haven't chosen Lewisham Hospital, have gone to King's or have gone to Guy's & St Thomas', with a small number in the south of the borough going to Princess Royal (Farnborough). I'm fairly confident that women will find it incredibly difficult to have to go to Greenwich.

He described the effect on the hospitals that women would choose to go to:

We believe that in fact most women will go to King's or St Thomas' and that will mean that these hospitals will become very large in terms of the size of their maternity service: so large that they will have to, if you like, double up their provision, particularly in relation to their provision of the obstetric rotas, which will make this a much more expensive service. That's also of course assuming that both of these hospitals have the capacity to extend their service. King's, for instance, is on a very restricted site geographically.

Ruth Cochrane, a consultant obstetrician, an exceptionally experienced clinician, described the efficient and effective working of Lewisham Hospital Maternity Unit. The unit offered a variety of high-quality services, and the prospect that these might be reduced to a single midwife-led unit in Lewisham Hospital without medical backup raised pressing concerns for her. She highlighted that it is in the nature of maternity work that emergencies are inevitable and unpredictable. The TSA proposals would result in women being transferred mid-emergency to another hospital – but none of the nearby hospitals had sufficient capacity to deal with all the women transferred if the Lewisham obstetric unit closed. Cochrane was of the view that this would endanger not only Lewisham women and babies but also those in the neighbouring hospitals already under great pressure because the service is overstretched.

Jessica Ormerod, a mother, former patient and lay chair of the Lewisham Maternity Services Liaison Committee, told the panel that Lewisham Hospital provides excellent maternity care. During the TSA consultation period her committee was invited by Lewisham Hospital professionals to join them in attendance at a TSA consultation meeting, She described the TSA team as failing to consider women's concerns. They were 'absolutely not interested'.

Another aspect the panel considered was maternal deaths. O'Sullivan was troubled by the spectre of such deaths, introduced unnecessarily by the Secretary of State in a speech concerning the proposed reorganisation of maternity services, in the House of Commons on 31 January 2013. O'Sullivan said:

> Just on the '100 lives' argument, I think to bring maternal mortality into this discussion is actually incredibly artificial. Maternal death is a very rare event in this country and I think to have even one would be a disaster. I don't believe there is any evidence to support the idea that larger maternity services are safer, are less likely to result in maternal mortality; nor do I believe there is any evidence that they are better quality.

He added that in seven years there had only been one maternal death at Lewisham hospital and that was of a mother who had not engaged with any service prior to presentation in labour.

With regard to children's services, O'Sullivan talked about the 'truly integrated' service in Lewisham, whereby hospital and community services are part of the same organisation. This had led to lower rates of admission for children, he said, 'less than 70 per cent of what we would expect'. He told the panel, 'One of the main things for me and one of the main risks, as I see, it, in terms of the implementation of the TSA proposals, is the loss of that integration.'

Sir Bruce Keogh had recommended to the Secretary of State a walk-in paediatric urgent care centre, removing the highly effective paediatric A&E and children's ward. In a written statement, Dr Tina Sajjanhar, a paediatric A&E consultant at Lewisham Hospital Trust, commented: 'The most disturbing thing about the TSA is that children's services are not specifically considered. . . . Sixty thousand children are now unplanned for in Lewisham.'

O'Sullivan also made a written statement, which is worth reproducing at length:

What is your job/role/occupation? How long have you been doing this for? Can you provide a brief summary of your background/experience?

I am employed by Lewisham Healthcare NHS Trust. My clinical job is Consultant Community Paediatrician (January 1993–current). I am Director of Service, Directorate of Children & Young People (January 2011–current)

I have worked for the community child health services in Lewisham as consultant paediatrician for over 20 years. My main role originally was to lead our child development and disability services. Early on I was also the medical representative for the Lewisham community health services on the Area Child Protection Committee (now this is known as the Local Safeguarding Children Board). In 1995 I set up the Lewisham service for children with autism spectrum disorder with our lead speech & language therapist. This has been nationally acknowledged as an example of good practice. I initiated and was centrally involved in the project to create a multi-agency community children's centre, where teams from Education, Social Care, Mental Health and community child health are co-located. Kaleidoscope

– Lewisham Centre for Children & Young People opened in 2006. Sited in Catford, near Lewisham Hospital, it is nationally a leading example for delivering services to support children with disability, emotional and mental health difficulties or other additional concerns. Children and families rely on networks within the health service and across agencies, working closely to support the child in need. Our community-based networks include the Special Needs Nurse Team and the Community Children's Nurse Team (the CCNT covers the three boroughs of Lambeth, Southwark and Lewisham). These two teams work very closely indeed with Lewisham Hospital and the tertiary hospitals in providing joined-up healthcare across hospital and community. We have a 'team around the child' (TAC) approach led through our multi-agency planning pathway (MAPP) and a key worker system that is much admired. The purpose of this approach and the key worker system is to put the child and family at the centre of planning care and to try to minimise the difficulties for them in coordinating care provided by often numerous, different services from Health (including mental health services), Education, Social Care, voluntary and other agencies. This is all part of the work to build protective pathways for vulnerable groups, founded upon cooperation between hospital and community health services, and educational and social care services.

What is your connection/interest/background/experience in the NHS?
My family is Irish. My father qualified in medicine in 1933 in Cork, Ireland. He worked in pre-war and pre-NHS

hospitals in Liverpool and Manchester. The 'poor law' hospitals became teaching hospitals where doctors and nurses learned their skills. GPs and consultants, however, made their living from payments for healthcare. In these pre-war teaching hospitals, doctors in training were given an honorarium and board and lodgings.

My father regarded the Second World War as a democratic issue against fascism. He volunteered for service and worked for six years as a major in the British Army, including in north Africa and Italy (Monte Cassino battle). When the war was over he was mentally scarred and unable to complete the professional exams (membership of the Royal College of Physicians) which he needed in order to become a hospital consultant physician. He became a GP in the new NHS in Manchester. As a child I was impressed with his admiration for the NHS and the equitable access it gave everyone in the community to GP and hospital specialist care. He used to provide community obstetric care also until the numbers of home deliveries in his practice became too few to maintain his skills. He kept his list of vulnerable elderly and made regular visits on them. One recollection I have is our family Christmas dinner being delayed each year until he had visited an elderly woman patient of his who was bed-bound. She got the first serving of the family Christmas dinner from my father – a Christmas bonus replacing 'meals on wheels' for that day. I accompanied him several years and this left a big impression on me. Flu epidemics saw him doing 20–30 home visits till the early hours.

I am committed to healthcare being provided by the

NHS, out of public taxation, free at the point of use without question or discrimination.

I became a community paediatrician not because I did not value hospital paediatrics and neonatology – I enjoyed both very much in training – but because I felt that children with health needs in the community (e.g. disability) deserved skilled care from well-trained children's nurses, therapists and doctors, working closely with both hospital children's departments and primary healthcare. Community-based care should aspire to the same high standards of training, research and high quality care that have long been established for hospital-based care. The ambition is to create safe and very good support networks that would help children, no matter what their disability or health need, to achieve their potential.

To me the term 'community-based care' is often used confusingly: safe community-based care for those that have significant health needs is when the community team and the hospital team work closely together and there is easy access to hospital services and expertise – Lewisham Hospital is bang in the middle of Lewisham community and in my view is an essential component of delivering high quality safe community-based care.

What is your connection/interest/background/experience in Lewisham and specifically, if applicable, with the hospital?
I have worked in Lewisham since 1993 in the role of consultant community paediatrician. From the beginning, my team forged links with the Children's Hospital, Lewisham (we were in separate NHS trusts until 2010). The

community team attend the Friday 'sit-down' ward round discussion at the Children's Inpatient Ward (and more recently the Neonatal Unit also) – we liaise over children on the ward requiring shared care, and discuss problems, forthcoming admissions, safeguarding, mental health and disability issues, discharge planning and complex care. Training posts rotate between hospital and community. There is a community paediatric presence for joint neonatal developmental follow-up outpatient clinics.

The aim is to join up care pathways for children across their community-based and hospital-based care, sharing information and informal discussion, sharing planned care, minimising admissions where possible and facilitating discharge planning.

In April 2010 the Community Services (children's and adult) merged with University Hospital Lewisham and the new trust, Lewisham Healthcare, became a new legal entity in August 2010. In January 2011, I became the Director of Service responsible for the Directorate for Children and Young People.

Why do you want to assist the Inquiry? (And/or see next question)

The TSA's proposals, endorsed by the Secretary of State, threaten the vital and supportive networks built up by our children's partnership, one that is mirrored in the maternity service and in the acute adult and care of the elderly fields. The TSA did not consult on children's services. The proposals affecting children were made without any analysis, scoping of present or future need, no recommendations and no consultation. They were treated as collateral damage, the consequences of the adult-based decisions of the TSA. Yet those proposals create radical change which will have a serious impact on 300,000 children aged 0–19 living in the South East London sector. The TSA process knowingly by-passed the expected standards for thorough clinical and public consultation when a significant reconfiguration of health service provision is required. North West London consultations over reconfiguration have taken more than two years. A reconfiguration of services in Manchester, which some say was handled well, took place over a 10-year period from consultation through to implementation. However appropriate the rapid crisis-intervention TSA and the Unsustainable Provider Regime may be for a single trust in trouble, it is wholly inappropriate for complex health and social care systems affecting services for 1.65 million residents, over 300,000 of whom are children.

In July 2012 the TSA was appointed to South London Healthcare NHS Trust, declared to be financially bankrupt. But he then took on an extended remit to investigate the wider, vastly more complex SE London sector in an impossibly short time frame. By using this regimen, he avoided due consultation process and avoided referral to the Health Scrutiny Committee. His proposals, endorsed by the Secretary of State, have major implications for Lewisham Hospital because he has selected this successful hospital for downgrading from major to local hospital, with loss of a wide range of services.

For children in SE London, there is no worked-out plan for their health needs. He has left Bexley children's service provision unclear and in dispute. Acute care of ill children in Lewisham and Greenwich is jeopardised – the two boroughs with the highest numbers of really ill children per capita in the sector. Tertiary pathways and relationships are strained and unclear. Inter-dependencies with social care and mental health have not been discussed nor recommendations made. The level of neglect for this population of children is breath-taking and irresponsible.

How are you able to assist the Inquiry – what is your expertise/ knowledge/specialism?

As outlined above, I have worked in Lewisham for 20 years and currently I am Director of Service for Children's Services provided by Lewisham Healthcare NHS Trust. I have worked throughout this time on inter-agency partnerships with Education, Social Care, Mental Health, the voluntary sector and parents. I have also worked within Health to promote functioning pathways across primary, community, secondary and tertiary healthcare. I am therefore in a strong position to assess the impact of the proposed changes and to analyse where the lack of due process and consultation has led to the severe shortcomings and dangers in the proposals.

What in your view were the original vision and principles underpinning the NHS?

That access to good health care should be a universal right and not dependent on the ability to pay; that our health system, including public health, research and training, should be funded from public taxation; that at the point of use, health care should not involve monetary fees; that provision of good health care is the responsibility of our Government, who should remain accountable for the NHS.

To what extent, in your view, have these been eroded by the internal market and recent moves to open the NHS to external market forces?

Firstly, I should say that the NHS is a very large and complex organisation, with major interdependencies with other sections such as Social Care. The complexity of the task is enormous: to be continuously embracing change and developing services, bringing in new research-based advances; managing the ever-increasing demands of a growing and ageing population; meeting changing public expectations etc. Where change is responsibly planned and it improves standards, I, and all doctors I know, embrace such change (and there are many examples available local to SE London).

However, until a few years ago the cost of administering the NHS and providing the infrastructure was 5–6% of the national NHS budget. I believe it is still less than 12% but has crept up with recent changes and costs of internal market, purchase/provider split and commissioning. This has been one of the most efficient health systems in the world. The cost of running health in the USA by comparison is over 30%.

It is important that NHS staff know the value of our work and aspire to maintaining our efficiency and do not waste resources. Over the last few years I have become more aware of the relative costs of investigations, drugs, location and type of care etc. This is positive.

However, changes have crept in that have significantly changed the nature of the NHS. Hospital and community providers have to act like separate business units within the NHS. They are commissioned for a range and volume of 'activity'. Prices (or 'tariffs') are put on as much of health provision activity as possible. The tariffs arrived at are unfair in that they disadvantage a hospital providing 'routine' local high-volume care for A&E, maternity and general paediatric and adult acute care. Tariffs proportionately pay far better for specialist care and elective surgery. Now hospitals are competing for 'customers' and will lose out financially if they don't. Like businesses they will 'go out of business' if they don't attract the right volume of activity and income. They have to prioritise financial survival over providing appropriate healthcare. The amount of time, skills, resources that are now concentrated in the NHS on these 'business' priorities is terrifying and is responsible for the rapid rise in NHS administration and infrastructure costs, alongside one other major financial pressure: the irresponsible PFI contracts.

I don't believe it is too late to save the NHS but the direction of travel has to be altered now before it is indeed too late.

In your view to what extent have these changes been openly debated?

In July and August, proposals came out from the TSA for a series of six workshops, promoted as clinical engagement forums. They were on hospital-based care and out-of-hospital care (later renamed 'community-based care'). There are a number of points to make on the process.

Firstly, there was no information whatsoever provided on children's health or social needs, nor the healthcare they require at these events. I raised this strongly. In the event, a single extra workshop was hastily put together which was then jointly for both children and maternity services. However, the only discussion at this and the other four forums I attended was tightly controlled around abstract 'blue sky thinking' around what would ideal healthcare look like. What was perverse about this was that we were told that the benefits of the blue sky thoughts would have to be realised within three years' time (at a time of extreme financial restraint in the NHS); and that at the same time one out of the five major hospitals would have to close. We were not allowed to question the validity of building a strategy around an assumption that numerous different ideal health and social care systems which did not exist would all be realised by three years' time. We were not allowed to discuss the impact of closing Lewisham's acute services – in order to risk-assess that option and plan accordingly – but were told nothing had been agreed. (Everybody I met knew that this was the major reconfiguration proposal that was pre-ordained (within the NHS London and TSA team), but no one could discuss it.)

The TSA draft proposals were published on 29 October 2012, and it was confirmed then that the major proposal was indeed to close down the acute and maternity services at Lewisham.

The TSA committed himself to an on-going debate about the proposals in the period between 29 October when his draft proposals were published and the 13 December close of the consultation period. After replying to the content of one or two clinical contributions, he stopped responding (other than TSA office acknowledgement or receipt), so that it was not possible to develop discussion with clarity. His attendances at Lewisham Hospital to meet with staff were marked by his stonewalling all objections, repeatedly saying that there was no alternative. The alternative from Lewisham Healthcare NHS Trust was not debated or costed, they were not invited to expand, were given inadequate data and no time.

Other legitimate and important challenges were similarly dismissed.

Data and Maternity: Data used was out of date and dangerously misleading – for example use of annual birth data from 2009–10 even though we knew the data for the following two years' births and births were rising fast. I was barred from challenging this data at a maternity forum in a 'risk analysis' discussion. I was told 'the data has already been agreed'. I had to insist that we include a risk that the data was wrong (which it was). In the end the wrong data had to be acknowledged.

I am aware that there were attempts to keep out of a maternity workshop the lay chair of the Lewisham maternity liaison committee, who had been invited by our Lewisham team to take part in the discussion. There were also complaints at the number of clinicians from Lewisham who attended. At Lewisham's insistence, those who had turned up took part.

On two occasions Lewisham clinicians were told to stop asking questions about the plan to close Lewisham Hospital and consequences or they would have to leave the meetings.

Travel times to hospital: It was evident in the TSA draft proposals, and in the TSA publicity, that the real impact on travel times for Lewisham residents to access care elsewhere was grossly underestimated. One key method was to use average travel times when 'there was no traffic' – an unrealistic event in inner south-east London: 'Private transport travel times are calculated on the basis of average speeds and travel times during periods of no traffic. Travel times may be higher during periods of busy traffic.' The overall impact was disguised by calculating the average increase in journeys for the 1.65 million people in the six boroughs rather than the impact for Lewisham residents (differentially greater for Lewisham with the loss of its hospital). There is a table for Lewisham, which demonstrates that this underestimates the impact by 5–6-fold. The most dangerous part of this is that average blue light ambulance times for Lewisham residents increases by 7.4 minutes instead of 1.4 minutes for SE London as a whole. This brings the estimated 95th centile figure (for times when there is no traffic) to less than 5 minutes short of the 30 minute maximum recommended by the LAS. This was not debated.

In your view to what extent would this process culminate in the destruction of quality of healthcare for the community of Lewisham and South East London?

I have no doubt that the proposals will worsen healthcare and health outcomes in SE London if they go through. One of the best-performing NHS hospitals will have been lost to the sector, which will be that much weaker, with less capacity and less flexibility.

The major justification provided by the TSA for the decision to take out Lewisham Hospital is that community-based care will transform SE London within 3 years, reducing hospital demand by 30%. There is no justification for such optimism, if that is what it is, and major NHS London individuals admit to that in private discussion.

So, if plans go ahead, a major hospital's very good acute and maternity provision will have gone, lost to the population of Lewisham and lost to the SE London sector, without any realisation of such ambitious transformation – which were it to be possible, would likely take 10+ years, not three.

There is a risk of increased morbidity and mortality, and worse health inequality, as acute and maternity services are harder to access for a relatively deprived, large population.

Networks built over 10–20 years in Lewisham will be fatally weakened before ever there is an opportunity to build a replacement set of networks in Greenwich between QE Woolwich and both Greenwich and Lewisham Social Care and other agencies.

Huge numbers of people will attend Kings, Guy's and St Thomas' and other hospitals because they are easier to travel to than QEH. This 'patient flow' was modelled for the 'A Picture of Health' reconfiguration in 2008/9 and was neither adopted nor repeated by the TSA. Lewisham care of the elderly services, reliant for success on pathways with Lewisham Social Care, will disintegrate as people are admitted to QEH and other hospitals instead.

Women wishing to deliver their babies in a safe environment, with emergency back-up should it be needed, will be unable to deliver in Lewisham and will have to travel much further. Midwife teams will not be able to deliver continuity of care between antenatal, labour and postnatal teams. Networks to protect vulnerable mothers, including teenage mothers, will be threatened.

What do the proposals mean to you and/or in your view to the community and/or to the NHS generally?
The proposals are so disturbing because there is such a lack of evidence to support them, and a lack of integrity based on thorough consultation behind them. There is an inevitability about SE London and Lewisham's NHS provision being much weaker having lost a major hospital.

There has been no professional analysis of the risk of rising mortality and morbidity should a busy successful unit like Lewisham close to the local population. There is evidence that there is such a risk (recent reports from Newark of significant rising local mortality in the three years since the A&E there started to transform from full A&E into an urgent care centre).

There will be greater inequality in the two deprived communities of Lewisham and Greenwich, with only one

A&E serving those two boroughs and also Bexley (over 750,000 population in total).

Without local access to a full A&E and admitting wards, Lewisham's ill population, adult and child, will be disadvantaged. Frequent attenders with long-term conditions such as sickle cell painful crises will have further to travel away from their communities.

The acutely ill elderly will have to be admitted to an out-of-borough hospital without direct links to social support networks and Social Care pathways.

The remaining A&Es, already bursting at the seams with work, will find it even harder to cope with the Lewisham population who attend there. Time-critical transfers to specialist centres will be in danger of delays in processing them on arrival at those A&Es (concerns raised by the LAS).

There will be less choice for women, who can no longer choose to give birth in an integrated midwife and obstetric unit.

A major justification for the poorly thought-out proposals is that Lewisham is failing to meet the London Emergency Standards. However, Lewisham is ahead of many hospitals already in working towards those standards and it is acknowledged by NHS London, Sir Bruce Keogh and others that no London hospitals currently meet them. Therefore, I am concerned that these aspirational standards are being misused, in support of a financial decision to close services at Lewisham. Instead a serious debate is needed on how to meet the overall pressures and demands in London and to move towards those aspirational standards. They could end up being part of a worsening of health care without due analysis.

Have you or someone close to you had any experiences of using Lewisham Hospital?
My main focus is on the families and children I have worked with professionally, though my family has used Lewisham and been treated well.

Is there anything else you think the Inquiry should be made aware of or anything else you wish to tell the Inquiry or have on record?
I have been shocked that some key players in the TSA process have supported the proposals wholeheartedly in public but have been apologetic in private and acknowledged the lack of fairness in the resulting decisions vis-à-vis Lewisham Hospital.

In conclusion, the panel shared the concerns expressed about the lack of analysis of the effect of the changes, in particular where pregnant women would actually choose to go to have their children, and the impact on the chosen hospitals, already struggling with capacity. This omission, the panel considered, had implications for costs – it was clear that many of the proposed changes would in fact be more expensive as well as less safe than the current provision.

The panel was extremely troubled by other evidence given in relation to maternity services, evidence that highlighted some of the evident dangers for women giving birth. These dangers exist even for the ostensibly healthy 12 per cent of women who meet the low-risk criteria of the Secretary of State's proposals for a midwifeled unit without emergency backup. Women throughout the borough would be put at risk by the implementation of the TSA proposals. The panel was also concerned that choice for pregnant women in Lewisham would be seriously reduced, contrary to the Government's 'fourth test' – patient choice.

The panel also queried the Secretary of State's purpose in introducing the emotive subject of maternal death when that clearly was not a concern in this situation.

The proposal for a small and safe A&E was a contradiction in terms and clearly did not accord with basic clinical requirements, or the needs of this disadvantaged community. It is not a concept recognised by the College of Emergency Medicine. It places the patient at risk and involves travel to more distant facilities already under intolerable pressure.

The panel was appalled that children, who form more than 20 per cent of the Lewisham population, were not planned for at all in the TSA proposals. It was unanimous in its view that the current system of care offered by the paediatric services in the hospital and in the community had been developed over many years so that the care it offered to the children of Lewisham responded exactly to their needs.

The panel agreed that the walkin paediatric urgent care service suggested by the TSA had no clear parameters, and was unsafe and unsustainable. Any such unit needed to be colocated with an emergency department, for which there were no plans. Standalone paediatric ambulatory care would predictably result in higher costs – a clinically suspect and more expensive downgrading of what existed.

The panel was astonished at the lack of consideration given by the Secretary of State to the effect of the TSA proposals on the vital, carefully developed, integrated network of care in Lewisham, which would almost certainly disappear if the proposals went through. The excellent care provided, developed over years, would be impossible to replace. The impact on the most vulnerable residents of Lewisham would be incalculable. Any replacement system would not be as good and will be absurdly and unnecessarily costly, contrary to the assertion of the Secretary of State that these measures need to be taken to save money. Reliance on the good work of charities would clearly be an inadequate alternative.

But the panel's main concern was the lack of proper statistics in the debate, which it described as astonishing. Where data existed, its quality and relevance was questionable. On the whole there simply had been no proper examination of the needs of Lewisham residents or consideration of the impact the proposals might have.

Overall conclusions

The panel was unanimous in its views about the approach taken by the TSA, the NHS medical director, Bruce Keogh, and the Secretary of State for Health, Jeremy Hunt, in their dealings with and decisions about Lewisham and Lewisham Hospital. It concluded that there was no legitimate medical or economic basis for the Lewisham decision by the Secretary of State and that none of the government's four preconditions – 'the four tests' – had been met. It criticised the minister and his department for having shown a cynical attitude towards the people of Lewisham in concealing the real motivation for the reconfiguration, and for the paperthin pretence that patient care would improve and patient lives would be saved. It asserted that it was incumbent upon the present administration to honour the original vision for the NHS:

> It will provide you with all medical, dental, and nursing care. Everyone – rich or poor, man woman or child – can use it or any part of it. There are no charges . . . no insurance qualifications. But it is not a 'charity'. You are all paying for it, mainly as taxpayers, and it will relieve you of your money worries in times of illness. (*1948 Bevan letter to every household*)

'That universal healthcare free at the point of delivery', the panel said, 'should remain the bedrock of government policy. That healthcare was not a commodity which can be subject to the exigencies of the marketplace and the profit motive and that patient needs and care are the paramount and determinative factor in healthcare provision.'

The judicial review took place a few days after the people's commission on 2–4 July 2013. The review eventually quashed the proposals for Lewisham Hospital on the grounds that the Secretary of State had acted *ultra vires* or beyond his powers, in going beyond the boundaries of the South London Healthcare Trust. On 29 October 2013 the three Appeal Court judges, Lord Justice Dyson (Master of the Rolls) and Lords Justice Sullivan and Underhill, dismissed the government appeal. On 30 October, it became clear during a House of Commons debate on the NHS in north-west London that the government would not be taking the case to the Supreme Court.

The people of Lewisham had won a great victory. But the coalition government then changed the law to allow a future administrator to cross the boundaries to another health trust area, though they slightly modified the powers of the administrator. It was a cynical demonstration of Whitehall's ability to continue to crush local protest and in the House of Commons alternative ways of handling the issues of cross-border involvement were brushed aside. Some nineteen NHS maternity units and fourteen A&E units have been closed or downgraded since May 2010. NHS England continues to make assertions about life-saving, claiming that 600 lives have been saved by centralised trauma units and that an ambulance may choose to travel further to obtain better and quicker expert care.

What the Lewisham health protest in all its many forms achieved in 2013, however, was a success that reverberated through the NHS and beyond. It convinced me personally, and I found it also began to convince other people that they were not powerless, that they could succeed in the law courts even if in the Houses of Parliament politicians had made no real impact. The desire for universal healthcare in the UK appeared to be still alive despite what was being done to the NHS in England and the continued cutbacks in social services. In this case local MPs and councillors were ready to fight back against central government. There was also genuine anger once people became aware that they had been 'conned' by the pledges of David Cameron and Nick Clegg not to embark on a top-down NHS reorganisation. The coalition looked tainted by it all, with two notable exceptions, Andrew George and Sarah Wollaston.

I began to believe as a result of the people's commission that the NHS as we have known it in England could be reinstated but there has to be specific legislation designed with surgical precision so as not to bring about yet another massive reorganisation. I started to think about a short Bill and began to work with Allyson Pollock, Peter Roderick and David Price, all three at Queen Mary, University of London and the Royal London Hospital in Whitechapel. As a result I presented two Bills to the House of Lords, the first on 28 January 2013 and the second Bill, of the same name with additional clauses, was presented on 16 May 2013 and is shown in Annex A.

Chapter 4

NHS Marketisation – EU and US

There are many people who are still unaware of how much in the 2012 NHS legislation system stems from the EU. The fact is that ever since Blair and Cameron promised referendums but subsequently withdrew their offers – over the 2005 Constitutional Treaty and the 2009 Lisbon Treaty respectively – the NHS has been opened up to EU intervention without establishing any resistance in Brussels to that intervention. It would be very surprising if UKIP do not exploit this issue at the 2015 general election, and there are already signs that they are going to do so.

EU competition law aims to prevent anti-competitive practices that act against the interest of consumers. Procurement law covers anti-competitive practices too. When combined they seek to protect the interests of both the consumer and the taxpayer. For many years the European Commission, by and large, stayed out of interfering in the NHS. It was assumed that this was politically too sensitive and in those days the Commission was not obsessed with market reform. The EU market was always open to exceptions, perhaps the most famous being the French railway system, where Paris never accepted EU intervention. Lately, however, it has been accepted that for 'consumer' the Commission can read 'patient'.

In 2006 Labour commissioned a legal opinion on the effect of EU legislation on the NHS. The Health Department's then commercial director, Ken Anderson, who had been involved with independent surgical treatment centres (ISTCs), told the *Financial Times* in January 2007: 'My personal conviction is that once you open up NHS services to competition, the ability to shut that down or call it back passes out of your hands. At some point European law will take over and prevail . . . In my opinion, we are at that stage now.'[58] As if recognising the truth of this interpretation on 13 December 2007, with not much publicity, the Department of Health issued a document titled *Principles and Rules for Cooperation and Competition*, running through which are EU legal positions which have become the law that operates in the UK. An advisory body, the NHS Co-operation and Competition Panel, was promised in 2008 and came into being in early 2009. Why did Labour allow this? The only explanation is that, having wanted to take Britain out of the European Community without a referendum in the early 1980s, which forced people like me to leave the party, they subsequently converted to the EU and in the process became more zealous than the Pope.

One body who was first to realise the impact of the EU on NHS policy was the campaigning group 38 Degrees, who also had the mechanism available to demonstrate public

---

58 *Financial Times*, 16 January 2007.

concern. They published their own legal interpretation of EU competition law: 'It is likely that, even as matters stand, and in view in particular of recent non-statutory reforms which increase the involvement of the private and third sector in health services provision, competition law already applies to PCTs and NHS providers.' They concluded that the 2012 legislation reinforced that view, adding that there was 'nothing in the bill which has or can have the effect of preventing the application of competition law' since prohibitions on anti-competitive conduct 'gives rise to actionable claims in the High Court by any person affected'.[59]

The advisory Co-operation and Competition Panel was reported in the *Financial Times* to have been applying its interpretation of the law since 2009 – by advising on NHS mergers and handling complaints about anti-competitive practices by hospitals and primary care trusts.[60] In this the Labour government was stealthily preparing for an EU market in health, something which Barbara Castle to her credit had predicted while Secretary of State for Health and Social Security during the 1975 referendum campaign. Despite being a member of the Cabinet, she was allowed to campaign for the 'no' vote, which she did not least because of the implications of the Common Market for the NHS. I disagreed then, wrongly, with her assertions and thought she was exaggerating. A lot happened which many people were unaware of over the following thirty-five years.

The NHS Operating Framework from the Department of

---

59 'In the Matter of the Health and Social Care Bill and the Application of Procurement and Competition Law', available at http://38degrees.3cdn.net/b01df9f37ac81ffb2e_zhm6bnldz.pdf (accessed 5 November 2014).

60 *Financial Times*, 27 and 29 July 2011.

Health for 2011 encouraged, for the first time, price competition below a maximum tariff. David Bennett, the new chairman of Monitor, who had been a senior partner at McKinsey and head of the Downing Street policy directorate and strategy unit under Tony Blair, gave an interview to *The Times* in February 2011 which described the regulator's new role in promoting competition. 'We did it in gas, we did it in power, we did it in telecoms,' he said. 'We've done it in rail, we've done it in water. So there is actually twenty years' experience of taking monopolistic, monolithic markets and providers and exposing them to economic regulation.' It was, he declared, 'too easy to say "How can you compare buying electricity with buying healthcare services?" Of course they are different. I would say ... there are important similarities and that's what convinces me that choice and competition will work in the NHS as they did in those other sectors'.[61] In an interview in the *Financial Times* he declared that ruling out price competition completely was 'neither necessary nor sensible'.[62]

Health economists were and still are divided over price competition. Zack Cooper of the London School of Economics and Political Science and Carol Propper of Imperial College London showed in different articles that there were some benefits from competition when patients were given a choice between hospitals which were being paid the same price per treatment. Propper's work on GP fundholding in the 1980s, by contrast, showed signs of a decline in quality when GPs were allowed to negotiate prices for treatment downwards. Research

---

61 *The Times*, 25 February 2011.
62 *Financial Times*, 28 February 2011.

in the United States showed that competition over price lowered quality. Cooper actually claimed: 'I am about as pro-competition in healthcare as you are going to find. But price competition would be a hugely retrograde step. To introduce it is not to learn the lessons from the NHS's own experience and from abroad.' Julian Le Grand, Tony Blair's adviser and an advocate of choice and competition in the NHS, also echoed the concerns.[63] Shortly afterwards, in a letter to *The Times*, the leaders of six health service unions expressed their 'extreme concerns' over price competition. The government had managed to unite reformers and opponents.[64]

The problem with the market zealotry of Andrew Lansley, aided and abetted by Cameron, Clegg and Oliver Letwin, is that there is no clear evidence to support their belief that competition between hospitals improves clinical quality. Professor Gwyn Bevan, professor of policy analysis at LSE, and a research student, Matthew Skellern, concluded in 2011:

> How patient choice has affected outcomes in elective surgery remains an open question; the exact role it should play in the policy mix is therefore unclear. Other open questions include: what is the cost effectiveness of competition, and how does this compare with other policies for increasing hospital quality? Furthermore, how might quality of care be improved in rural areas (e.g. Cornwall) where competition is unalterably weak, or for types of care for which it is more

63 *Financial Times*, 6 January 2011.

64 Nicholas Timmins, *Never Again? The Story of the Health and Social Care Act 2012 – A Study in Coalition Government and Policy Making* (Institute for Government, 2012), p. 80.

difficult to design effective competition? More research is required before conclusions can be drawn about the effect of recent reforms on hospital quality, let alone about the merits of Mr Lansley's proposals further to extend competition.'[65]

On 28 February 2011 Lansley asked the former Health Secretary Alan Milburn, who had left the Commons and was the independent reviewer to the coalition on social mobility, if he would be a candidate to chair the commissioning board. Milburn responded, 'Do you think I have the letters M.U.G. tattooed on my forehead? Why would I use my political capital to rescue you from the mess you have made of yours?' While he was against all-out opposition to competition he told *The Guardian*: 'Either these policies are an evolution or a revolution, but they cannot be both'.[66] That is undoubtedly true, but since they represented a movement from an internal to an external market, they were not evolutionary. The two are different in concept and in execution. This was a revolutionary change and it was implemented with revolutionary fervour, as well as the crass incompetence that all too often accompanies revolutions.

Nigel Edwards, the acting chief executive of the NHS Confederation, underlined the degree to which under the 2012 legislation it was intended that the state would 'be withdrawing from the day-to-day management of health care', with the service becoming 'like a regulated industry' on the lines of

---

65 Gwyn Bevan and Matthew Skellern, 'Does Competition between Hospitals Improve Clinical Quality? A Review of Evidence from Two Eras of Competition in the English NHS', *British Medical Journal*, 9 October 2011.

66 *The Guardian*, 16 March 2011.

telecommunications, water and the energy industries. It could, he warned, 'trigger a major reshaping of the way care is delivered with services closing and changing'. 'I do not think most people have grasped the scale of this change,' he continued. 'By 2014, the NHS will no longer be a system which still contains the characteristics of an organisation. Instead it will be a regulated industry in which that management chain no longer exists.' Amid 'any willing provider', services would have to become more responsive to patients. But in a system with no real financial growth that would mean that new providers would have to replace existing ones. 'There will have to be an element of Joseph Schumpeter's "creative destruction".'[67] The destruction duly came and it is continuing in the NHS. Its harbinger is an unproven belief in the benefits to the NHS of competition.

Cameron later stated that 'put simply, competition is one way we can make things better for patients. This isn't ideological theory. A study published by the London School of Economics[68] found hospitals in areas with more choice had lower death rates.' The Prime Minister seemed unaware that this paper had been challenged repeatedly, not just on its conclusions but on its methodology, most recently in an article in *The Lancet*.[69]

The Prime Minister also seemed unaware of concerns in the

---

67 *Financial Times*, 16 January 2011.

68 Zack Cooper, Stephen Gibbons, Simon Jones and Alistair McGuire, 'Does Hospital Competition Save Lives? Evidence from the English NHS Patient Choice Reforms', LSE Health, January 2010.

69 Allyson Pollock, Alison Macfarlane, Graham Kirkwood, F. Azeem Majeed, Ian Greener, Carlo Morelli, Seán Boyle, Howard Mellett, Sylvia Godden, David Price and Petra Brhlikova, 'No Evidence that Patient Choice in the NHS Saves Lives', *The Lancet*, 17 December 2011.

medical profession on the latest evidence from the Netherlands. The Dutch competition authority (the NMa) has had the effect of fragmenting service provision and impeding the provision of high-quality care.[70] We have learnt recently of a €7.7 million fine levied on the Dutch GP association for a 'bad case of anti-competitive behaviour', which was the association's efforts to ensure that all areas of the country were adequately provided with GP services.[71] The Dutch Patients' and Consumers' Federation called for the involvement of competition in healthcare to be urgently reviewed. The 2012 legislation heralded by the government as primarily being about enabling and freeing GPs ended up facing calls for its withdrawal from the Royal College of General Practitioners.

The government, throughout the passage of the 2012 legislation, kept attaching far too much importance to a few studies whose conclusions and methodology had been professionally challenged. Earl Howe, a junior health minister, partially quoted a Professor Smith, an economist, writing in a 2009 health report to the OECD that 'competition can take many different forms, and sharpening competitive forces is likely in general to be an important tool for most health systems'. Yet Smith intervened to suggest that for completeness and balance this quote ought to include his previous sentence too: 'True market competition introduces a set of raw incentives that carries serious potential for adverse outcomes for many aspects of healthcare.'

---

70 Tony Sheldon, 'Is Competition Law Bad for Patients?', *British Medical Journal*, 20 July 2011; Tony Sheldon, 'Dutch GP Association Is Fined €7.7m for Anticompetitive Behaviour', *British Medical Journal*, 16 January 2012.

71 Sheldon, 'Dutch GP Association Is Fined €7.7m for Anticompetitive Behaviour'.

Many in the health professions want to proceed with care and caution over the introduction of competition policies in healthcare. They are not Luddites nor wedded to the status quo; they are ready to see further experiments in competition but they want an objective evaluation and an evolutionary approach that was the hallmark of the early proposals in the 1980s for an internal market in the NHS to build in studies and cost comparisons to aid efficiency. For many health professions the question was why and on what evidence the coalition government was endorsing the abandonment of the concept of the internal market and instead introducing a full-blown external market with no credible evidence basis for such a decision. This growing perception of a distortion of the evidence basis was not helped when the government appointed two non-executive directors to join the chair and the CEO of Monitor who were both former McKinsey senior managers and had specialised in privatisation; the chair and the CEO had the very same background, suggesting that skills in privatisation were considered essential qualifications for a senior role in Monitor. Nor when in 2010 private equity investors in New York received a personal invitation to enter NHS provision from a former NHS director of commissioning through a presentation on profit opportunities arising in the UK healthcare sector, which stated:

> In future, the NHS will be a state insurance provider, not a state deliverer. In future any willing provider from the private sector will be able to sell goods and services to the system. The NHS will be shown no mercy and the best time to take advantage of this will be in the next couple of years. GPs will have to aggregate purchasing power and there will

be a bid opportunity for those companies that can facilitate this process.[72]

Treasury officials in private, when one met them in off-the-record forums, were beginning to speak openly about their growing concerns over delivery of the £20 billion efficiency savings by 2015. They knew well that the Department of Health was in turmoil and that undergoing massive reorganisation does not usually provide efficiency savings. There was an even more important aspect – an organisation in which its most dedicated supporters feel alienated is even less likely to accept continued pay restraint, pension reform and other key government priorities.

The Prime Minister let it be known within his own circle that he had offered some big concessions to Nick Clegg to compensate for the rebuff of losing the referendum on the alternative vote, and he expected a demand to drop the Health and Social Care Bill, which he would have acceded to. But Clegg never put this as his priority and chose other concessions.

Of course, after the unprecedented legislative pause, actually halting the Health and Social Care Bill would have been a political rebuff, a U-turn over which the Labour Party would be bound to crow for a while. But the Prime Minister showed when he ditched the coalition government's forestry proposals that that sort of criticism only lasts for a few days and is soon forgotten. The political prize for abandoning the Health and Social Care Bill for Clegg would have been immense. A relieved workforce,

---

72 'Opportunities: Post Global Healthcare Reforms', Apax Global Healthcare Services conference, October 2010.

a united health profession and an accompanying readiness to adopt a reform programme within existing legislation at a faster pace than ever before would have been major advantages worth far more than temporary political embarrassment. A new government in 2015 with a positive reform programme could make the NHS work effectively, as soon as the right legislation was announced. There is no appetite within the health professions for a status quo. What they all want is coherent evidence-based reform, but they see no prospect of it happening.

The Labour government had introduced *Principles and Rules of Cooperation and Competition*, which effectively applied competition law to contracting for patient services, but whereas PCT commissioners were encouraged (but not obliged) to commission services through competitive markets, the new clinical commissioning groups under the coalition were required to introduce such markets. This was despite the assurance given in the Lords by Earl Howe that

> clinicians will be free to commission services in the way they consider best. We intend to make it clear that commissioners will have a full range of options and that they will be under no legal obligation to create new markets, particularly where competition would not be effective in driving high standards and value for patients. As I have already explained, this will be made absolutely clear through secondary legislation and supporting guidance as a result of the Bill.[73]

But these words were shown to be worthless by the regulations

---

73 Hansard, HL Deb, 6 March 2012, vol. 735, col. 1691.

which followed. These regulations, when they emerged, only mirrored Andrew Lansley's speech in 2005,[74] where he very clearly spelt out his intentions to open up the NHS to competition but which he was forbidden in the run-up to the election of 2010 to mention.

The draft regulations were then published on the instructions of Jeremy Hunt when he became Secretary of State. Max Pemberton perceptively wrote up the true situation in the *Daily Telegraph* on 1 April 2013:

> What was now clear was that the regulations effectively forced CCGs to put all services out to tender to the private sector and forbade them to favour the NHS as the provider . . . Most experts agree that there was no meaningful change. GPs are allowed to keep some services within the NHS, but only in particular circumstances, such as when no private sector provider comes forward to bid. Everything else is up for grabs. It will take time for this change to slowly spread throughout our health care system, but it will.

Indeed Hunt deliberately began to slow the system so that it would not be fully operational until after the general election.

It has been very difficult in 2014 to establish exactly what is likely to emerge from the whole commissioning experiment. The government is clamping down on announcements for fear of frightening the electorate with the implications. But the shape of it all is starting to become clear. Practice plc, the UK's largest

---

74 Available at http://www.andrewlansley.co.uk/newsevent.php?newseventid=21 (accessed 5 November 2014).

operator of privatised NHS practices, terminated its service in Camden Road surgery following its acquisition of the business from the American healthcare giant UnitedHealth because it was more profitable to invest in providing commissioning support services. Other GPs were left to pick up the pieces amid criticisms of the closure procedures and patient discontent, with some claiming to have been given the wrong medication.

In Staffordshire four CCGs – Cannock Chase, North Staffordshire, Stoke-on-Trent and Stafford & Surrounds – will, as mentioned, hand over £1.2 billion of taxpayers' money for contracts lasting ten years in vital cancer services and end-of-life care. The organisations involved do not just contract to provide a service; they also design the system. Commercial and NHS organisations can bid for the contracts, and the CCGs were open to independent commercial organisations, third-sector groups or consortia. Whoever wins the cancer contract will then have to transform the provision of cancer care in Staffordshire and Stoke and manage all the services along existing cancer care pathways for the first two years. Then the provider will assume responsibility for the provision of cancer care in the expectation of streamlining the service model. The charity Macmillan Cancer Support is advising the four CCGs on the cancer contract. This large contract in Staffordshire was matched by one in East Anglia worth at least £800 million to provide older people's services in Cambridgeshire and Peterborough; the four shortlisted bidders include Virgin Care and a consortium comprising two NHS trusts and Care UK.

It was announced in November 2014 that University Hospitals of North Midlands Trust, Staffordshire's main hospital provider, and the Royal Wolverhampton Hospitals Trust were pre-qualified bidders for both contracts, and that other bidders which passed the pre-qualification stage of the tender for the cancer pathway contract, worth £687 million, were Interserve Investments, CSC Computer Sciences, and UnitedHealth UK (which has generally been known as Optum since a rebrand last year). This contract will initially cover breast, bladder, lung and prostate cancer, and expand by the fifth year to all cancer services. For the end-of-life care contract, worth £535 million, the independent sector pre-qualified bidders are Virgin Care, CSC Computer Sciences, Health Management, Interserve Investments and UnitedHealth UK. These organisations will be submitting outline bids, which are expected to be awarded in the summer of 2015 after the general election.

The huge costs involved of carrying out these tenders, and the process itself, have created considerable opposition and a fear that if they went to commercial contractors after ten years they would be primed for privatisation. The tender project's director of clinical engagement, Jonathan Shapiro, surprisingly told the *Health Service Journal* in July 2014 that he believed most services would continue to be provided by the same organisations as they are at present. If that should prove to be the outcome it would only show how predetermined the whole project is.

There is much confusion in the debate over competition about the precise meaning of the term 'privatisation' in the context of the NHS. The main thrust of the Health and Social Care Act 2012 was for marketisation and commercialisation of the NHS, and Michael Gove claimed after he became Chief Whip that no privatisations had taken place. There was, however, one unequivocal and deplorable act of privatisation brought in by the coalition government, namely the sale of PRUK Ltd to the US private equity company Bain and Company, in which former presidential candidate Mitt Romney has been heavily involved for many years. It is now under foreign commercial majority control with the British government retaining only 20 per cent of its shares. This privatisation is unlikely to be the last, however, if the Conservatives continue in government after the next general election. When advertising for a new chair for NHS Blood and Transplant (NHSBT), for example, it was made clear that candidates should have privatisation experience. So not only is Gove's categorical denial on behalf of the government that they have never privatised any part of the NHS wrong, even on the Conservative definition of having to sell the asset, they have established a clear-cut precedent for further privatisation. When contract renewals come up there can be no doubt that existing contractors will come forward with proposals for a change of ownership, no doubt claiming that in the process they will keep the NHS logo.

PRUK Ltd was a Department of Health-owned company that held two separate but related subsidiary companies – Bio Products Laboratory (BPL) and an American company, DCI Biologicals Inc., bought by the Labour government in 2002. Together they formed a supply chain for the production and supply of plasma-based medical treatments. The privatisation went ahead despite vigorous protests that this was counter to the best interests of the NHS, proven by past experience with the supply of contaminated blood products to NHS patients.

Since the emergence of new variant Creutzfeldt-Jakob disease (nvCJD) in the UK, it has been a sensible public health policy of successive governments not to use UK plasma. A return to using UK plasma is theoretically possible in the next couple of years and having ownership of a US company could have been a way of creating and investing in the best technology so as to put this into action in the UK when it again became feasible, relying on UK voluntary blood transfusion donors. But that is not the policy chosen and the reason was a narrow interpretation of NHS interests based on saving necessary short-term investment. BPL was formally transferred from NHSBT to a limited company, Bio Products Laboratory Limited, in 2010 to come within the PRUK 'group' and thereby under the same umbrella organisation as DCI Biologicals.

BPL has had Department of Health funding (through NHSBT) to remain solvent; from 2003 until its transfer in December 2010 it made a cumulative loss of more than £100 million and required over £95 million cash support from the Department of Health. A further cash injection to support the business of £58 million was given at the time of transfer, but there was insufficient investment.

The price of the sale of PRUK, quite apart from the damage to health policy, raises serious questions. The UK taxpayer spent £540 million in 2002 to establish the company. It was offered for sale at a suggested £200 million, £90 million now and up to £110 million payable after five years. That second payment may never be made, for its payment is contingent upon profitability over the next few years measured by post-tax profits. The UK government retained a 20 per cent share in the company and will make some capital gain when sold, but there is no guarantee of a UK presence in the ownership of the company into the future.

For tax efficiency reasons, private equity firms usually extract their profits not as dividends after tax, but as interest payments on long-term debt. The interest is tax deductible, and will be high enough to wipe out profits so as to minimise tax liability. PRUK appears to be structured in this way, for while its sales have soared since it was carved out from NHSBT in 2010, its audited accounts continue to record small losses rather than post-tax profits and its debt obligations are recorded but not in enough detail to understand.

On the face of it, therefore, Bain has bought PRUK for less than one sixth of its worth based on the money put in. In fact the US plasma source should have been worth far more than the initial £540 million, since the plasma trade has seen high growth since 2002. It also appears that more taxpayer funds may have been put in since PRUK was carved out into a blood products company. Bain will almost certainly wait five years to avoid second payments, during which it will build up the company with one objective: fattening it for a future sale. That is what private equity companies do, which is why I argued against health investment on the advisory board of Terra Firma.

Examination of the company's US products shows already the sort of short-termism one would expect. Also concerns have developed that DCI Biologicals Inc. as a commercial plasma supplier performs to market standards; these standards are low and its planned transformation into a high-grade source has yet to be and may never be undertaken.

DCI owns a series of harvesting stations in low-income US towns which buy plasma at market price: a base donation of $15 (with small bonuses for repeat donations, to a total of $200–$300 per month for eight donations) for an invasive procedure that takes between two and four hours excluding the frequently lengthy wait to be harvested. At these prices and in these circumstances only the desperate and derelict contribute to the supply: desirable donors do not frequent the areas where these collection stations are located and have better sources of income. We know from the plasma seller talkboard 'How much at DCI Biologicals' something about the donor base:

Post#130: 'Overall I would say its 65% legit people who need some extra help for gas and food and 35% to feed a habit but that could just be my branch.' [Albuquerque]

Post #149: 'I am a relocated ER RN selling plasma so I can get my license here locally – broke, single parent. Most of these people are mentally challenged addicts & alcoholics. Street people. The company definitely parks itself on skid row on purpose.'

Post #129: 'You have lost your mind if you think everyone they let in through there to give plasma is "suitable". As long as they claim to have never been an IV drug user or homo and can account for all their tattoos they are good to go. Problem is PEOPLE LIE.'

Post #169: 'The state health organization should close this place down!!! They are allowing people with prison tattoos to donate plasma and are not requiring any documents as to when and where tattoos were gotten. But ask for medical documents for a scar over 10 years old. This is supposedly the life saving plasma given to our mothers and children. OMG this is inexcusable and the FDA should step in and close this place down. All they are doing is funding the drug use in our community.'

When will Conservative and Liberal Democrat politicians learn from our own disastrous experience of contamination of blood supplies? Donors of doubtful background are very unlikely to answer honestly questions about their past health. With hepatitis, when we had no screening test donors had to be asked about being yellow or jaundiced. We had no way then, as now, of testing for the virus that infected so many NHS patients and relied on honest replies from our voluntary donors. Patients suffering from haemophilia need constant infusion of the clotting factor, which they do not have, to stop them bleeding and that clotting factor was only be found naturally in blood.

The nature of blood and plasma donations and supplies renders them vulnerable for transferring unknown or undetectable viruses that cannot be found on screening and cannot be killed before being put into a patient's blood vessels. Among haemophiliacs, cases of AIDS were identified in Spain and America in recipients of prisoner plasma which was also used in the UK. One of the few ways of reducing the risk is to take blood from people who are less likely to harbour viruses that will harm patients. This is best achieved by self-sufficiency and a readiness to pay for it. This is why in 1975 when minister in the Department of Health I adopted a policy, of which Parliament was informed, of investing for self-sufficiency in blood products and it was a tragedy that the policy was abandoned a few years later, initially without Parliament being told. The underlying ethical and moral arguments for self-sufficiency have never been better expressed than by Richard Titmus in his magnificent book *The Gift Relationship*. In the UK we do not pay donors, we rely on the voluntary spirit and a cup of tea after the blood is taken. We could if there was an emergency easily increase supply but we keep the NHSBT on a tight budget and if we can buy cheaper we do so. That is fairly safe if the suppliers are international pharmaceutical companies, but less so for smaller entities.

The major strategic concern for government ministers should be a more secure supply to the NHS of key products. The principal risks to the supply chain of products to the UK relate to the withdrawal of a major supplier from the UK market entirely. That is why we should have kept BPL and invested what was necessary in it. To take normal human immunoglobulin (IVIG) as an example, the NHS need is a small proportion of the global demand (around 7 per cent), and the government's own study before the sale admitted that demand

> will itself be subject to influences in the wider market in particular, multinational companies will consider how they can maximise their profits and, at times of high demand and limited supply, may wish to take their product elsewhere. EU procurement rules may limit the UK's ability to respond to this by price renegotiation.

This means that it is vital that Bain should be approached by any new government in 2015 and told in the case of them selling the government will wish to expand its 20 per cent share to percentage levels which could reduce the likelihood of any sudden withdrawal from the UK. New markets and medical uses for the product mean that we cannot assume that supply will always outstrip demand.

The current contractual requirement that suppliers to the NHS hold three months' stock provides insurance against temporary jolts to supply, and allows a little time to investigate the best response to a major longer-term shock, but that stock-holding insurance would be far better if it was increased. Continued state ownership would have given a better security of supply. It is now essential that Bain are made aware by the government, as a shareholder, that it expects more investment, quality improvement and wider product range through research and development. Repeated outbreaks of fatal disease among haemophiliacs testify to the inadequate standards delivered by the 'self-policing' global commercial plasma industry. Participating companies prioritise cost minimisation so that they can afford to sell at the market price and still make a profit. Consequently, stringent protection for all users of those plasma products must be exerted and with a 20 per cent holding the UK government has a fiduciary responsibility to do so. The risks of the global plasma trade are well documented and the measures needed for safe practice are clearly established[75] so that there can be no excuse for a developed country, like the UK, as a shareholder and user, to expose the patients of a publicly funded healthcare service like the NHS to the risks of relying on anything less than the best and safest blood products. None of this appears to be happening, nor should anyone be surprised. In the vast area of commercial markets there is a place for private equity capital, as I saw when on the advisory board of Terra Firma, but not in a predominantly publicly provided NHS. PRUK was the wrong privatisation to the wrong company. Let us pray that NHS patients do not experience through continued negligence

---

75 'Blood Plasma Safety: Plasma Product Risks and Manufacturers' Compliance', statement by Bernice Steinhardt to the Subcommittee on Human Resources, Committee on Government Reform and Oversight, House of Representatives, 9 September 1998.

anything like the suffering of those of our fellow citizens treated for haemophilia who were transfused unknowingly with the hepatitis C virus or HIV with tragic consequences for their lives.

In 2013 the then chair of the Royal College of General Practitioners, Dr Clare Gerada, wrote of the Health and Social Care Act:

> This is about free markets, not healthcare. It is predicated on making money, not on doing the best thing. The NHS is a system that channels resources according to need. What the Act does is change it to a system that channels resources according to what makes money. Competition is the vehicle for changing it. I feel that it's more important than ever that we do everything we possibly can to challenge the perversities of this marketisation. The money needed to run this new market will take away money from services.[76]

On 5 April 2013 I sent an email to several key members of the Labour shadow Cabinet whose portfolios were impacted detailing my concerns about the implications of trade agreements for the NHS, particularly those being negotiated with Canada, which were near to completion, and the EU–US Transatlantic Trade and Investment Partnership (TTIP), which was further off. Internationally as well as nationally it was time for the labour movement, I believed, with fellow social democrats in Europe to consider the emerging bilateral trade agreements that had

---

76 Quoted in Nicola Cutcher and Lucy Reynolds, 'The NHS as we know it needs a prayer', OpenDemocracy website, 19 February 2013.

been negotiated in unprecedented secrecy. My major concern related to the social market and the legitimate democratic choice for incoming governments to protect public provision in health and other social and educational services without the constraint of international legislation. I am not against the market's contribution to global economic growth and prosperity. Free trade has its place. The problem is, as Pascal Lamy argued in October 2014, that 'failing to make clear that the TTIP negotiations too are about regulatory harmonisation was a huge blunder. Negotiations need to be transparent if they are to calm public suspicions.'[77]

I forwarded three documents which I believed had important implications for any reinstatement of a democratic NHS in England after the next general election and for maintaining the existing NHS in Scotland, Wales and Northern Ireland. First was a statement against the intense investor protection rights that were being included in the Canada–EU Trade Agreement (CETA) dated February 2013. I was concerned that in the list of European organisations and groups signing up, there were none from the UK. The second document was from the Canadian Labour Congress written in March 2012 and was about how fragile the protection of Canadian public healthcare – and by implication the protection for our NHS – is in the CETA context. The third document, written in 2011 by a German academic lawyer, provided a legal assessment of some detailed aspects.

Much concern focused on the lack of definition of what 'public purpose' could be construed to mean, especially when

---

77 Pascal Lamy, 'Transatlantic trade negotiators should own up to their ambition', *Financial Times*, 27 October 2014.

there was already much private involvement; in other words the difficulty of drawing or asserting the lines. Clarity, in my view, was essential if there was any hope of the 2012 health legislation in the UK being checked, let alone reversed by the next government.

Another focus for concern was the negative listing approach and process, which is different from the GATT's positive listing approach. Negative listing would mean countries having to state which services they are going to liberalise. In the CETA this meant that governments (at all levels in Canada) would have to name what they want excluded and there could be no later adjustments. The same would apply in the UK. The 2012 legislation for NHS England had already been deliberately made compliant with CETA and this was the key concern, despite pledges made in the House of Lords, as to why the government had not made any real changes in the revised regulations that were debated in the House of Lords on 24 April. This emphasised that we were not only dealing with a national political challenge but a coordinated international one as well. I see no incompatibility in my reservations over this with a lifetime's support for world trade agreements under the GATT and the WTO, which has added to UK and world prosperity. Those negotiations are primarily about tariff reduction. CETA and the TTIP include regulatory convergence, which for some in the US is code for curbing anti-globalisation activists in ways that are not acceptable.

I was not clear that the shadow Cabinet fully understood that what was in CETA would be taken as read in relation to the NHS for all future EU trade agreements, including the TTIP, negotiations for which were just starting. I would like to say my then concerns were taken seriously, but it was only when

I saw Frances O'Grady, the general secretary of the TUC, that I sensed genuine commitment and found that the TUC was actively involved with other European trade unions.

In my judgement, British politicians have not taken anywhere near enough interest in the CETA negotiations, and in part this is because the negotiating is done by the European Commission. We have far more allies in Canada on the issue of safeguarding public healthcare, and therefore the NHS, than ever we could expect from the US with its private health provision. In November 2014 the new European Commission refused to be bound by the past, and signature of CETA was blocked through the collective effort of the European Trade Union Confederation.

President Obama with the EU heads of government and the Commission will go on pushing a trade agreement through 2015 and overall this is good for the UK. It is possible over the NHS to negotiate a *broad exemption* from the impact of such a trade agreement. It is not easy to define an exemption in great detail without seeing the negotiated texts, which is very difficult to achieve given the secretive method of TTIP working. The truth is that regulatory convergence is something the EU conducts day by day as part of the social market. There is a framework of law which is understood, but in the EU the disillusionment, notably with the Investor–State Dispute Settlement (ISDS; see below), stems from a deeper disillusionment with US legal practice and US data privacy legislation, coupled with the US healthcare industry's wish to penetrate the different EU healthcare systems, which owe much to the social market. Here 'social' is not a shibboleth but an integral part and the TUC are rightly suspicious of those who want to inhibit even the right to switch out of a contract without cost when it is time expired.

It has become clear that there is a far-reaching implication for any NHS marketisation because of the direction of travel within the EU towards trade links with the US based on an ever-greater application of pure market principles in the healthcare field. This direction has been challenged by the leader of the German SPD, Sigmar Gabriel. It was apparent in September 2014, just as the CETA was about to be agreed, that the German coalition was not on board. Other social democratic parties within the EU, particularly the Austrians, protested. Will the UK coalition rethink?

If the NHS again became the 'preferred provider', this would force the European Commission to make an exception for it. The Commission usually makes exceptions when faced with powerful enough lobbying from the European Parliament and European trade unions. If the NHS regains its 'preferred provider' hallmark after 2015, the EU pressure for marketisation of healthcare can be not only resisted but probably stopped in its tracks. Due to the strength of the SPD and its position in the German grand coalition led by Angela Merkel. Jean-Claude Juncker, the President of the European Commission, has curbed the power of the actual negotiator on the Commission by specifically giving control over the ISDS to a vice-president, Frans Timmermans. There is a readiness to shift in Brussels.

It has been claimed that GP commissioning would not constitute an economic 'undertaking' (which would fall under EU competition law), although it would do so 'when [GP practices were] competing for services as providers'[78] It has also

---

78 Simon Burns (minister of state, Department of Health), Public Bill Committee, Health and Social Care Bill, Eighteenth Sitting, 15 March 2011, col. 766.

been claimed that competition law would not prevent vertical integration or an expansion in a provider's range of services, and that competition and choice 'would strengthen incentives for providers to work together in integrating services'.[79]

The test of whether an entity is an 'undertaking' for competition purposes in the EU is whether it is engaged in an 'economic activity' and whether it performs an *exclusively* social function based on the principle of national solidarity. As commissioning consortia develop using the autonomy available to them under the Act, it is by no means clear that they would be exempt from competition law. In the 2002 *BetterCare* case[80] the UK Competition Appeal Tribunal rejected the argument that the local health and social services trust did not constitute an undertaking simply because it was carrying out a social function in purchasing care for the disadvantaged. The tribunal argued that the trust was using 'business methods' in its contracting. Academics claim that this decision 'suggested that European competition law will apply to an entity that participates in markets, even if the purpose is a social one, and even if the market is highly regulated.'[81] The situation was later complicated by the Office of Fair Trading (OFT), which decided that competition law had not, in fact, been breached because the discriminatory prices involved had been set by central government, which was not an undertaking given its exclusively social functions. This must heighten the importance of the new freedoms being

---

79 Ibid.

80 BetterCare Group Ltd *v.* Director General of Fair Trading [2002] CAT 7.

81 Elias Mossialos, Govin Permanand, Rita Baeten and Tamara K. Hervey (eds), *Health Systems Governance in Europe: The Role of European Union Law and Policy* (Cambridge University Press, 2010), pp. 321–2.

offered to English commissioning consortia in terms of pricing outside of the NHS Tariff. Similarly, the mixed role of consortia as both purchasers and providers of services would fall foul of the OFT's 2004 clarification on the application of competition law to public bodies, in which it said that it would drop cases against such bodies engaged only in purchasing and not the provision of goods and services in a particular market.[82]

If commercial enterprises are involved in a health system this heightens the possibility that competition law will apply. This has been raised in the context of competing sickness funds within the Netherlands' social insurance system. The European Health Management Association has expressed concerns that the threat of the application of competition laws may limit healthcare reform across Europe.[83]

It has been stated that

if a Member State chooses to operate a health service predominantly on the basis of social solidarity, decisions of the bodies comprising it will not be covered by competition law. If, however, a Member State decides to introduce competition – for example, by contracting services out to competing suppliers of health care provision or by creating a competitive internal market – then competition law will apply, as the various bodies involved will be acting as undertakings.[84]

---

82 Office of Fair Trading, 'The Competition Act 1998 and Public Bodies', Policy Note 1/2004.

83 Richard B. Saltman, Reinhard Busse and Elias Mossialos, *Regulating Entrepreneurial Behaviour in European Health Care Systems* (Open University Press, 2002), pp. 44–5.

84 Mossialos et al., Health Systems Governance in Europe, p. 323.

This does not preclude the Article 86(2) exemption in the EU Treaties for 'service of general economic interest' (SGEI), used to defend socialised ambulance services against competition complaints from private competitors, in view of the real risk that the private providers would 'cream-skim' the market and not provide a universal service. This exemption was first highlighted in Article 16 of the Amsterdam Treaty, signalling that services of general economic interest should be free to 'fulfil their missions' if competition law would otherwise prevent this.[85]

The reference in Clive Efford's Bill to SGEI needs re-examining. The OFT has summarised the current situation, saying that NHS entities are unlikely to be considered to be engaged in economic activity if they provide universal or compulsory services, with the same benefits for all regardless of contributions; and if they operate with a redistribution mechanism between the relevant entities in order to remedy financial disparities.[86]

Competition law is complex and, to a degree, unpredictable in its application as case law develops. Whatever ministers may assert to the contrary, the continued rise of competition and choice in the NHS will inevitably be matched by a rise in legal conflicts and litigation costs for the NHS. European competition law already impacts to some extent upon NHS providers, in their private sector activities, and as NHS and independent providers begin to compete more actively for NHS 'business' competition rules may become directly applicable. Giving

---

85 Ibid., pp. 326–7.
86 Office of Fair Trading, 'Working Arrangements between the OFT and the CCP', undated.

Monitor concurrent powers with the Competition and Markets Authority (CMA) will also blur the distinction between the enforcement of NHS competition rules and the enforcement of UK and European competition law. Where are the Conservative Party's Eurosceptics on these issues of vital concern? Where is UKIP? When Britain joined the European Community it was always envisaged that our health service would remain outside the scope of European law. This principle has been eroded by both Labour and Conservative governments in recent treaty revisions. It is a vital UK interest to clarify and restate member states' competence in this area. Instead all we see is the European institutions' desire to extend their own competence. We have witnessed this in the very damaging effect of the Working Time Directive on the hours of work of health professionals who have hitherto been willing to accept longer working hours. But it has also been due to the gradual commodification of European health systems since the 1980s. This issue must be opened up in the 2015 general election campaign.

The unprecedented scale of the marketisation enterprise in England eventually came to light on 19 February 2013, when the Department of Health published the regulations under Section 76(6) of the Health and Social Care Act that opened up the NHS in England to competition. The political assurances given during the passage of the Bill were shown to be worthless. The regulations force health commissioners to open up virtually all services to competition, either through competitive tendering or using the 'any qualified provider' (AQP) market. The AQP market operates as the 'choose and book'[87] system, which provides patients with a shopping list of services from which to select their treatment.

From 1 April 2013 commissioners were required to advertise[88] new contracts, then judge the bids received based on published criteria. The new regulations effectively closed down the possibility of awarding a contract without competition, saying that this could only occur in exceptional circumstances (namely emergency situations or when no other provider is capable of providing the same services).[89] They also pulled arrangements between NHS bodies into the new competition regime, contrary to assurance given by Andrew Lansley to CCGs in 2012.[90]

The new regulations granted Monitor sweeping statutory powers as a regulator to intervene and enforce competition.[91] Monitor is able to decide when commissioners have breached competition regulations and has the authority to set aside contracts, to stop arrangements that it deems flawed and to impose competitive tendering and the offer of AQP. This is despite Monitor's role as regulator being changed in Parliament from one of 'promoting competition' to 'preventing anti-competitive behaviour'. Many predicted at the time this was a distinction without a difference.[92]

---

87 www.chooseandbook.nhs.uk

88 National Health Service (Procurement, Patient Choice and Competition) Regulations 2013, Regulation 4.

89 Ibid., Regulation 5.

90 Letter from Andrew Lansley to prospective CCG leaders, 16 February 2012, available at http://falseeconomy.org.uk/files/lansley-ccg.pdf (accessed 6 November 2014).

91 National Health Service (Procurement, Patient Choice and Competition) Regulations 2013, Part 3.

92 Hansard, HL Deb, 12 October 2011, vol. 730, col. 1678.

All the talk of GPs having flexible powers to choose the right provision for patients was set aside with the regulations forcing competitive markets across the board, barring only very exceptional circumstances. The assumption without evidence-based proof that a greater choice of providers is better for patients was the abiding passion behind the regulations. In reality, what little international evidence there is shows a poorer service for patients.

I believe that the TTIP should not in principle contain the controversial investor protection clauses. They are potentially too damaging to the NHS to be tolerable and so if they are included then there must be exemption for the NHS. The question is: will we exact enough influence through the European Parliament and through the European Commission under President Juncker?

As explained in my book *Europe Restructured*,[93] I have always been in favour of British membership of the EU but as chairman of New Europe opposed membership of the eurozone. In my judgement we will eventually have to hold an in-or-out referendum, but there is serious negotiating needed in 2015–20 before that vote can be taken. The British people are loyal members of clubs, but not afraid to restructure a club or an institution to better suit different circumstances. They are wise enough to steer clear of deadlines, such as 2017, which Cameron wants to impose on our EU partners. The 2011 Referendum Act was the best legislative achievement of the Conservative–Liberal Democrat coalition and the

---

93 David Owen, *Europe Restructured: The Eurozone Crisis and Its Aftermath* (Methuen, 2012)

Labour Party now supports it as well. It ensures there can be no new transfer of power to the EU without a referendum. This is a huge safeguard against ever-greater integration. In renegotiating from 2015 a better deal for the UK we need politicians in all parties who are not ready to tolerate damage to the NHS. People recognise environmental hazards are better dealt with within the framework of a single nation, or even a small number of nations. A new aspect of Britain's negotiating position is that at long last no political party wants to join the eurozone, but it has been correctly made clear that the UK does not want to damage the interest of those EU member states who are in the eurozone or those who might wish to join it. If our politicians stand their ground on this basis we will not be seen to be just pushing our own self-interest. We will be upholding our right to democratic self-government in our country while accepting that others in the eurozone may well wish to, and probably need to, move in a more federal direction. The younger generation of Britons in my experience have no deep-rooted dislike of foreigners; they are content to live in a multi-racial Britain and are neither jingoistic or chauvinistic. They are ready to be convinced that in the twenty-first century we may need different forms of economic self-government, but the emphasis is on being convinced. They want no more spin doctors' tricks, no sleights of hand with the wording or timing of an eventual referendum. The Scottish people have shown the way for the UK. A referendum campaign can be passionate and engaged. It can, as in Scotland, enthuse the young and produce a massive turnout of more than 80 per cent. But an EU referendum involves twenty-seven other countries.

The pace of any negotiation over an in/out referendum is

impossible to predict in a single year. Cameron would have been wiser to set a negotiation period of a five-year parliament. There is a real risk still of a collapse in the eurozone with some countries having to leave while the UK attempts a renegotiation. The coalition has fixed in law a five-year parliament. It would be prudent to stick with this for another five years. Yet it is now clearly the settled will of a majority of the electorate that before the putative end of the next parliament in 2020 there has to have been an in/out EU referendum. The best outcome for the 2015 general election would be if all the parties likely to make up any new government commit before May 2017, if there has not been a referendum, to invoking Article 50 of the Lisbon Treaty. This gives the obligatory two years' notice of an intention to withdraw from the EU but allows negotiations to continue. This would be coupled with a commitment to hold an in/out referendum no later than December 2019.

The EU itself is constantly debating and negotiating all aspects for renegotiation, particularly its social market. The relevant words are in the EU Treaty, Article 2(3):

> The Union shall establish an internal market. It shall work for the sustainable development of Europe based on balanced economic growth and price stability, a highly competitive social market economy, aiming at full employment and social progress, and a high level of protection and improvement of the quality of the environment. It shall promote scientific and technological advance. It shall combat social exclusion and discrimination, and shall promote social justice and protection, equality between women and men, solidarity between generations and protection of the rights of the

child. It shall promote economic, social and territorial cohesion, and solidarity among Member States.

I have a long-held interest in the social market and helped create the Social Market Foundation in 1989. To celebrate its twenty-first anniversary I wrote a pamphlet and much of what I wrote in 2010 is still highly relevant. Though the term 'social market' has won acceptance, the shifting balance of political forces within the Council of Ministers and in the European Parliament, mainly between social democrats and Christian democrats, ensures that the parameters of such a market cannot be set in concrete. It must be able to reflect the voters' will as represented in national and European elections. Also any worthwhile organisation adapts to changing circumstances and learns from experience. There are many different health systems within the EU. The mistaken idea that the NHS could be bound by EU directives on competition or procurement is recent. The Labour government's formal legal opinion in 2006 (see above) offers a snapshot of how the treaties were interpreted then; now, after the changing position over the CETA, the new Commission has an opportunity to readjust the EU's attitude to healthcare as a market-driven competitive service and instead redefine healthcare in terms closer to those of a publicly provided service.

The crucial country that will shape such a social market, at least until its federal elections in 2017, is Germany and the coalition of Christian Democrats and Social Democrats led by Angela Merkel. The 'Rhineland capitalism' and its associated social market economy which prevails in Germany, Austria, the Netherlands and part of Belgium was well described in

2002 by Will Hutton in his book *The World We're In.*[94] But there have been shifts in attitudes within the political parties in Germany since then over the social market. The Social Democrat Chancellor Gerhard Schroeder, interestingly, made the most significant changes towards the 'Anglo-Saxon model': emphasising the market and the need within the eurozone to be competitive with internal labour market disciplines. Today his fellow Social Democrats are over TTIP challenging this model, which was broadly endorsed by the UK Labour government between 1997 and 2010. When the Christian Democrats, under Angela Merkel, formed a coalition with the Social Democrats after failing to win outright in September 2013, it meant reducing the emphasis within the coalition by Christian Democrat leaders on market forces and a minimum wage was conceded. Meanwhile the liberal Free Democratic Party (FDP), the Christian Democrats' coalition partner until the 2013 election, is no longer represented in the Bundestag falling below the 5 per cent threshold. It is, however, still in the Liberal grouping in the European Parliament with the British Liberal Democrats. That defeat carries a warning to Clegg, Alexander and Laws, not to follow their continental liberal attitudes in pursuing market models in the NHS. Their neo-liberal attitudes are very different to those of Paddy Ashdown and Charles Kennedy, both former Liberal Democrat leaders.

Some Conservative politicians in the UK have not wanted to accommodate to anything like a common social policy accompanying the Single Market. The left/right language of British politics does not fit easily with social policy being

---

94 Will Hutton, *The World We're In* (Little, Brown, 2002), pp. 259–64.

determined by the wording of European treaties. A minimum wage used to be controversial between the parties in the UK, thankfully no longer. It is a sign of the times that this has now been introduced in Germany by the Christian Democrats in the coalition government. It is becoming an EU-wide social policy but fixing its level must surely remain a member state responsibility, just like fixing the balance in tax levels and social security provision. Also the balance between financial incentives and redistribution must remain a political judgement on which political parties within the EU will differ.

After the 2015 general election there may still be cross-party divisions on the EU. In April 1993 Labour, then in opposition, championed a tactical device in the House of Commons that tied ratification of the Maastricht Treaty to acceptance of the Social Chapter. This device, which the Liberal Democrats went along with, attracted many Conservative rebel MPs who wanted neither ratification of the treaty nor in some cases to remain in what was due to become the European Union. Those Conservatives were ready to vote for acceptance of the Social Chapter, despite their opposition to it, in order to destroy any prospect of ratification. What emerged was described by the then Prime Minister, John Major, in his autobiography as 'a madhatter coalition'.[95] Though the vote did not prevent the treaty becoming law it presaged divisions to come and became known as 'the ticking time bomb'.

Another aspect of renegotiating health and social policies within the EU after 2015 concerns the German Constitutional Court. A press release of 30 June 2009 from that court made an

---

95 John Major, *The Autobiography* (HarperCollins, 1999), p. 315.

extremely important ruling on the Lisbon Treaty. It laid down general guidance as to how it might be possible to establish a narrow interpretation for future social policy in its widest sense, setting limits and parameters, perhaps in a new protocol, within the framework of the Lisbon Treaty. The court's judgment read:

> European unification on the basis of a union of sovereign states under the Treaties may . . . not be realised in such a way that the Member States do not retain sufficient room for the political formation of the economic, cultural and social circumstances of life. This applies in particular to *areas which shape the citizens' circumstances of life, in particular the private space of their own responsibility and of political and social security*, which is protected by the fundamental rights, and to political decisions that particularly depend on previous understanding as regards culture, history and language and which unfold in discourses in the space of a political public that is organised by party politics and Parliament. To the extent that in these areas, which are of particular importance for democracy, a transfer of sovereign powers is permitted at all, *a narrow interpretation* is required. This concerns in particular the administration of criminal law, the police monopoly, and that of the military, on the use of force, fundamental fiscal decisions on revenue and expenditure, the shaping of the circumstances of life by social policy and important decisions on cultural issues such as the school and education system, the provisions governing the media, and dealing with religious communities.[96]

---

96 Emphasis added.

In the English translation of the full German Constitutional Court's ruling, paragraphs 395–7 spell out the legal situation. Those who want a social market which can protect the NHS also want the social part to be developed more within each member state and less by the European Commission, and they should seek to enshrine this German constitutional ruling as part of a UK negotiation strategy. It would help to give us negotiating credibility in Europe on a very sensitive issue if we were to work with the grain of the court's ruling (see Annex D for further details of the court judgment).

The UK under all governments has tried to maintain a position that social, employment and health policies should remain with the member states and not pass to the EU. Now more member states believe that the detail on matters such as maternity leave, the working week and the rights of part-time workers should not be fixed on an EU-wide basis, although there are good arguments for a general injunction to member states to ensure some level of provision is made. The same must apply to health, not specifically mentioned by the German court but covered by the wording in italics, 'areas which shape the citizens' circumstances of life, in particular the private space of their own responsibility and of political and social security'. Variations between member states in these areas would not affect the broadly level playing field of a single market. Much the same argument applies to the detail of the Working Time Directive, which it can be argued is already hampering the running of the NHS and the emergency services.

The UK could modify its new Supreme Court to cover constitutional issues, either by evolving precedent or by specific legislation. To do so would strengthen the UK position that there must be defined limits to ever-greater integration. That is very different from trying to change the wording of the EU treaties, which aspire to 'ever greater unity for the *peoples* of Europe'[97] – desirable perhaps but not obtainable. Ever-greater integration between governments is not and could never be part of an EU treaty unless the EU became a single federal state.

Before a sensible negotiation in the EU on social legislation can occur we need in the UK to dissect and to determine, as far as possible on an all-party basis, which aspects of the social market economy need to be covered by EU treaty language and which are best left for member states to determine through their own procedures. As part of a UK negotiating strategy for reform of the EU, German Constitutional Court statements and reservations offer a rich seam for Britain to mine, for within them we will find ways for enabling our own Supreme Court after only five years' existence to mirror and build on the German experience. In addition our Supreme Court can take a position on some of the interpretations of the wording of the treaties by the European Court of Justice. Words cannot be beyond challenge: it is a central element in the British system that Parliament legislates and courts interpret the wording of the legislation. It is a costly myth in terms of EU membership to go on cleaving to the oft-quoted words that we in Britain do not have a written constitution. We have in the EU treaties a constitution, and never admitting that meant we never developed before 1973 the necessary counterweight of a supreme court.

It is worth examining in detail what actually happened in Germany in September 2014. In order to head off the growing

---

97 Emphasis added.

opposition in the SPD and German trade unions to the Investor–State Dispute Settlement (ISDS) terms, the Economic Affairs Ministry – headed by SPD leader Sigmar Gabriel – issued a joint position paper on the TTIP along with the DGB, Germany's trade union confederation including the country's largest trade unions like IG Metall and Ver.di.[98] The paper, while praising elements of the TTIP, pledged on the ISDS: 'Investment protection provisions are generally not required . . . In any case, investor–state arbitration and unclear definitions of legal terms such as "fair and just treatment" or "indirect expropriation" must be rejected.' Significantly, in approving the paper, party delegates insisted that its provisions should also be applied to the EU–Canada free trade deal (CETA), which had by then been largely concluded and was due to be signed off by the outgoing Commission President, José Manuel Barroso, and the Canadian Prime Minister, Stephen Harper. CETA, which many see correctly as the blueprint for TTIP, includes an ISDS. Interestingly, the German government and the European Commission were at odds over whether national parliaments will need to ratify CETA alongside the European Parliament. The Commission said no, but Berlin argued that as a 'mixed agreement' with some of the issues, goods and services covered by CETA falling outside of the EU's sole jurisdiction, the Bundestag and Bundesrat should also get to scrutinise the agreement and vote on it. The German government warned that it was willing to go all the way to the ECJ on this issue. How this

---

98 Bundesministerium für Wirtschaft und Energie / DGB: 'Transatlantic Trade and Investment Partnership (TTIP): Anforderungen an Freihandelsgespräche zwischen der EU und den USA unter der Berücksichtigung von Nachhaltigkeit, Arbeitnehmerrechten und der Gewährleistung der Daseinsvorsorge.'

dispute plays out will have direct relevance to what can be done to insert a healthcare amendment in CETA.

The Austrian parliament also passed a motion dismissing the need for an ISDS in both CETA and the TTIP and called for the preservation of 'high social, data protection and environmental minimum standards' in the TTIP. The outgoing European Trade Commissioner, Karel De Gucht, rejected calls for CETA to be renegotiated, arguing, 'If we were to reopen the negotiations, the agreement would be dead,' and singled out the German government, the European Parliament and incoming European Commission President Jean-Claude Juncker for indulging a 'populist, emotionally charged' debate.[99]

The new President of the Commission, Jean-Claude Juncker, seems determined to reopen the negotiations even in the face of opposition from the Commission itself. The social market in the EU may be starting to see a new and much-needed strengthening of the social side, and that need not weaken a true market where it can be applied. What is highly worrying, however, in all this is the position of the chief executive of NHS England, Simon Stevens.

Stevens faced questions from the public when launching the *NHS's Five Year Forward Plan* on Radio 4's *Today* programme. Caroline Molloy, the editor of OurNHS on the openDemocracy website, was obviously listening in and reported that presenter Sarah Montague read out a question:

> People are concerned, not least because of trade talks that are going on which could mean that the NHS is forced to open

---

99 *Frankfurter Allgemeine Wirtschaft*, 25 September 2014.

up under TTIP to American companies . . . Does Simon Stevens think he can be unbiased on TTIP given his links to a pro-TTIP lobby group when he was at UnitedHealth?

On the programme, Stevens refused to be drawn on his views or his lobbying on TTIP. 'You haven't actually answered,' commented Montague.

Simon Stevens began his career in the NHS twenty-six years ago. He was Tony Blair's health adviser in No. 10, and then 'President of Global Affairs' at the American private healthcare giant UnitedHealth until taking up his post as chief executive, appointed by the chairman of NHS England and Jeremy Hunt, the Secretary of State for Health.

According to Physicians for a National Health Programme in the US, Stevens was a founder member of the Alliance for Healthcare Competitiveness (AHC) – a US lobby group pushing for the inclusion of health in the TTIP treaty, as discussed in Chapter 4. He also acted as a spokesman for the AHC's pro-TTIP position. In September 2011 – as health industry TTIP lobbying was already underway – the *Star Tribune* in Minneapolis reported, and re-reported by OurNHS: 'A coalition of US health care businesses, including Minnesota-based UnitedHealth Group and Medtronic, proposes to rebuild America's battered economy by selling the country's 'health ecosystem' internationally. The Alliance for Healthcare Competitiveness (AHC) wants the US government to build its foreign free-trade policy around the health care industry.' The paper quoted Stevens commenting on behalf of the AHC that 'the worldwide need for health care in aging populations will lead to a demand for goods and services that can drive sales of American insurance, medical devices and record-keeping technology'.

The *StarTribune* went on to admit:

The US health care system . . . is beset with skyrocketing costs and inefficiencies. Americans currently pay more for health care and rank lower in life expectancy and infant mortality than much of the developed world . . . The call to rebuild the US economy by selling pieces of what is generally considered a broken health care system struck some experts as a bit awkward.

The AHC themselves said in their 2013 submission to the US Trade Representative Office:

The proposed TTIP is of great interest to our members as the European Union is the site of nearly a third of world health spending, the principal buyer of American exports of health products, and is experimenting with new approaches to health care systems . . . The health sector is the largest single component of the world economy. In 2010, according to the World Bank, health accounted for almost $7 trillion of $63 trillion in global GDP . . . The health sector will be one of the world's main future drivers of demand and growth . . . This gives the United States a significant opportunity . . . We know that as hospitals gain rights of establishment abroad, they become natural buyers of American medical devices, natural users of American health IT systems, natural telemedicine customers of US-based hospitals, and natural partners for American doctors and medical schools. Trade negotiations on behalf of the sector as a whole have the potential to unleash powerful synergies.[100]

The AHC argue that US trade negotiators must demand 'full elimination of tariffs on all health goods', from pharmaceuticals to furniture, and that 'non-tariff barriers . . . generally appearing as regulatory policies' are 'the principal barrier [and] powerful obstacles'. So they demand 'regulations to help generate competition', adding: 'Trade agreements are an opportunity to address these problems; further open health care services markets; impose disciplines on regulatory authority, including rules for technical standards and recognition of qualifications; and ensure that trade in health care services will reach its extraordinarily large potential.'

The AHC at their most explicit argue: 'Trade agreements should cover health care. Exemptions from government procurement coverage should be minimal, rather than broadly and ambiguously drawn for "health care" or "public health".'

It is extraordinary that the chief executive of NHS England can so recently be associated with views like these.

Although the actual TTIP negotiations are being kept under close wraps, the demands of groups like the AHC seem to be being heard. Cameron and his coalition ministers – though repeatedly pressed – have refused to exclude or exempt healthcare from the TTIP, saying it is 'unnecessary'. The AHC say that American corporations currently lack 'effective international

---

100 Alliance for Healthcare Competitiveness, 'Transatlantic Trade and Investment Partnership', submission to the US Trade Representative Office, 10 May 2013.

disciplines' to ensure that governments do not 'offer advantages to state-owned enterprises [which I think it is fair to assume means organisations like the NHS] at the expense of private capital, including foreign or foreign-invested competitors'.

Labour appears to want to bring in a policy of the NHS as 'preferred provider' – yet the AHC believe it creates 'major competitive distortions' and should be stopped by the TTIP. 'Fundamentally, health providers and insurers should be able to establish operations abroad in the form of their choice with no artificial limits . . . Trade agreements like TTIP are an opportunity to create such a system.'

The AHC say regretfully that 'the WTO and the procurement features of recent trade agreements have achieved relatively little in health . . . An open trading world for [healthcare] services would create a large new flow of revenue into the United States from foreign operations and from telemedicine.' There is a particular focus on enabling 'cross-border provision via telemedicine' and allowing health data to be shared across frontiers.

In the name of promoting 'innovation' in drugs, medical apps and other telemedicine gadgets, AHC also says that in many countries, 'US Food and Drug Administration . . . reassurance . . . of dossier review and product approval should be sufficient', without the need for 'onerous' additional requirements such as the 'publication of clinical evidence in peer-reviewed journals'. It is notable that telemedicine and medical apps also feature strongly in Stevens's NHS *Five Year Forward View* – as do US-style private 'accountable care organisations' – though the evidence base for such approaches is currently very weak.

The AHC – which includes the main international pharmaceutical companies among its members, as I know from my period as a non-executive director of Abbott Laboratories in Chicago – is also keen to prevent 'a downward spiral in terms of prices for medicines', recommending that 'trade agreements including TTIP . . . eliminate or at minimum reduce use of price limits'.

As the chief executive of NHS England, Stevens has a responsibility to tell us his current views when he gives a 20 minute Radio 4 interview. Answers to questions about his strong links to pro-TTIP lobby groups like the AHC are necessary, so patients can judge whether to trust him to protect the NHS. They are not likely to go away and OurNHS are correct to demand answers. The fact that NHS England is a Quango does not exempt its Chief Executive from questions. But all this demonstrates that NHS England cannot remain totally autonomous and preferably should become a Special Health Authority, SHA, and be answerable directly to the Secretary of State for Health.

Chapter 5

SOS: Save Our Surgeries

On 5 June 2014, coming up to my seventy-sixth birthday, I found myself again on the march over the NHS. This time, along with many fellow patients of the Jubilee Practice in Commercial Road, Tower Hamlets, we walked to Kingsley Hall, Bow. I have been a patient at this practice for nearly fifty years, as were my three children until they left home to live in Lewisham.

The problem we patients faced was an acute one. NHS England had delivered Dr Naomi Beer and her fellow GPs a financial threat so dire, that regretfully they had concluded that their practice would have to close within a year. This was a consequence of the decision to phase out the Minimum Practice Income Guarantee (MPIG), and we felt it could not be allowed to stand with respect to this specific practice and other good GP practices in east London. The MPIG was introduced in full in 2004 as a top-up payment to those practices that faced a reduction in their hospital levels of funding under the new GP contract. The coalition government, having reviewed the position, had taken the view that the MPIG was unfair, because, under this payment system, two surgeries in the same area may be paid very different amounts of money per registered patient, despite serving very similar populations. They intended to phase it out over seven years.

The government claimed that the majority of practices would in fact gain extra funding under these changes and that the decision to phase out the MPIG over seven years was taken so as to enable the small number of practices that lost funding to adjust gradually to the reduction in payments. The money from the MPIG would be reinvested into the 'global sum' payments made to all general practices.

The MPIG decision was in fact taken by the Department of Health just before NHS England came into operation, which meant that implementing the decision was left in the hands of NHS England. They had made two recent statements which were factually incorrect, as reported by *GP Online*: the national spokesman for NHS England declared the MPIG was being phased out because it 'takes money from GP practices with the heaviest workloads and sickest patients', and an NHS England spokeswoman had said:

At the heart of this is ensuring all patients have access to high quality GP services that are close to home. These changes – which are part of a national policy – will help make GP funding more equitable across London, and the majority of practices will gain as a result. It means that practices will be paid fairly according to the number of patients they care for and their needs.

Just prior to the start of the meeting in Kingsley Hall a senior representative of the Royal College of General Practitioners had explained to me as an examiner for the college the nature of an award that the Jubilee Practice had just received. He described the practice as 'outstanding, not just good'. He was shocked that the Department of Health and NHS England could be so incompetent as to have made a decision that carried with it the inevitable financial consequences for such an excellent practice. This episode sadly highlights what has become an acute problem for us all: the sheer incompetence of NHS England. Wherever one looks and wherever they act, incompetence is becoming their hallmark.

At the meeting the mood was one of stunned incomprehension after all the stories were told in some detail of the effects, and for dependent patients this was a bombshell. Most attending the mass meeting had long-term disabilities, and many were clearly unwell. Some had walked or come in wheelchairs over considerable distances under the slogan SOS: Save Our Surgeries. It was for me yet another impressive demonstration that people still have power. Could I be witnessing, first in Lewisham and now in the East End of London, a popular movement that just might be able to mobilise across political parties and across class barriers? Could it grow and eventually demand of politicians that they reinstate the NHS? That thought on the march began to firm up as I listened to Dr Beer speak to those in the hall in simple, direct terms:

Today, we are marching for our local surgeries. We have shown what it means to stand together. I am so proud that we are able to show the nation [TV cameras were present] who and what we are and what people who work together can achieve. This is also about the heart of the NHS. It is all about values. The values at the heart of the NHS and of our nation. What successive governments have done is put corporate values at the heart of our NHS, replacing a language of collaboration, compassion and service for the good of all with the corporate language of competition, service delivery and productivity. When you set out to achieve something, you first decide on your core values. This determines your goal or function and the structures follow. In the NHS today, this is all the wrong way round. Structures come first and values have to lag behind and fit in somewhere. This is why GPs in east London and across the country are in the position we find ourselves in today – defending and justifying our very existence because the Secretary of State hasn't the power or necessarily even the will to act on our behalf, despite the evident justice of our cause.

So let us hold our heads up high and continue to fight to tell the public what is really happening to their NHS so that the values we treasure can be put back at the very heart of this much-loved and fantastic institution.

I wrote the next day to Earl Howe, the government's health minister in the House of Lords, saying that I hoped he would speedily intervene to ensure the unintended consequences of the initial decision were reversed. NHS England had not yet come up with firm proposals, although they had already made clear they would not be able to meet the practice's needs. As of now, I told Howe, this practice was heading for closure – a totally unacceptable outcome for any fair-minded person.

At the Royal College of General Practitioners (RCGP)

on 3 October 2014 Beer spoke again, this time to her fellow practitioners, knowing that while there had been by then some financial easing the underlying problem remained. This was a woman who had led her team of GPs throughout the fight. They had known that the threat to close their practice had to be based on transparency. They revealed all their remuneration and they demonstrated with the help of their very skilled practice administrator that their practice faced such a diminution in professional standards that they would rather close than continue. Their protest had produced a little more money for two years, sufficient for them to wait and see what next year at least produced. Her task now was to convince her Royal College to reform the MPIG, and an extract of what she said follows:

Let us not be ruled by fear or cynicism. Nothing is a reality until it happens. The very fact that I stand before you today, an ordinary GP, undistinguished in any sphere and previously known only to her patients, is a testament to the improbable yet possible. I represent a practice that, like yours, works hard to ensure that its patients receive the best service we can give within our means. We work in the East End of London. Our population is undoubtedly needy. The day we discovered that NHS England was implementing the MPIG withdrawal in such a way that would immediately compromise our survival, we faced the choice to fight or go under. To us, this was a matter of justice – justice for our patients, justice for our staff.

We were, however, astonished at the lack of noise coming from our representatives over this issue. The RCGP Put Patients First campaign was and remains a welcome exception.

Patients should be at the centre of the concern. So we made the decision to fight. We knew we were good, we knew we could prove it, we value what we do and most importantly our patients do too. We also had the support of our patients, our local MPs, our local GP colleagues and our CCG, who, historically, has always taken an enlightened and constructive approach to local primary care. We were extremely fortunate in this support. United action is always strongest.

With increasing annoyance we heard the frankly untrue but oft-repeated mantra of the health ministers and NHS England that the MPIG withdrawal was all about equity. Get this for equity – Tower Hamlets, with one of the most deprived and fastest-growing populations in the country, had almost 25 per cent of the threatened practices in the country. It is set to lose about £6.7 million out of its primary care budget due to the current funding changes. Some practices are set to lose almost 25 per cent of their funding. Many of you will share similar stories of cuts to funding that will affect patient care. 'Equity' has been defined with a totally skewed reference to health needs. The much-trumpeted redistribution into the global sum doesn't go anywhere near compensating us for the costs involved in delivering care to a population like ours that, for the poorest patients, mean death at eighteen years younger – eighteen years – than patients from the most affluent areas of the country, who are right now benefiting from the redistribution of our MPIG and maximum QOF[101] payments! We do not have

---

101 Quality and Outcomes Framework, a system for the performance management and payment of GPs.

the benefit of other more lucrative avenues of income to keep us going – if the global sum is what is going to keep us alive then either the calculation around global sum has to change to fairly reflect activity or we need to move to more localised budgets which reflect population need. There are no other options. . . .

Money helps and good outcomes help and where the two motivations have combined we have achieved astounding results for our populations. Tower Hamlets has gone from one of the worst boroughs in the country for diabetes and heart disease outcomes to the best due to the injection of performance-related incentives. We have saved far more money in stroke prevention than any stroke unit can ever achieve – however good! Yet GPs have been beaten with sticks, blamed for every ill of the health service, told we are greedy and lazy. This is how greedy – we worked out that for every patient contact, a GP in our practice receives in their pocket less than £2. Excuse me if I specifically address my remarks to our NHS England CEO at this point, but £2 per contact, Mr Stevens – what kind of system can you dream up that can do better than that? And for that paltry amount we work unreasonably hard. So hard that GP burnout is the biggest growing reality that threatens our service. . . .

Coming from a deprived area I would also like the Carr Hill formula properly weighted. [This formula was developed in 2003 and can create as much as two-thirds differences in funding.] This should not be beyond our wit but is it beyond our will? It should not be. We are and should be accountable but we do not have to sit dumbly and let our paymasters define everything about what we do. We need quantitative and qualitative evidence and *we* with our patients need to define the vision for our future.

That same conference heard Dr Maureen Baker, chair of the RCGP, say that the college had identified up to 600 practices where more than 90 per cent of the GPs were aged sixty or over, many of whom would retire over the next twelve months since GPs on average retire at the age of fifty-nine. In 1964 when the Labour Party won the general election I, having stood as a parliamentary candidate in an unwinnable seat, was back at St Thomas' Hospital as a neurology registrar. All around us in Lambeth GPs were up in arms over their conditions of service. The new Minister of Health, Kenneth Robinson, faced a crisis in general practice which he dealt with extremely well. Such a crisis is developing now for 2015.

The 2012 legislation has had a devastating effect on GPs' morale and yet to hear the coalition government talk they are still quite unaware of the depth and the gravity of the crisis. There are 340 million GP consultations a year, a figure that has increased by 20 per cent over the last two years. Dr Baker referred to general practice as providing a dam that prevents the NHS being flooded, and that so far much of the dam wall had been hidden from the public. They see the flooding downstream in crowded A&E departments but when GP practices close she warned we will see whole chunks of the dam fall apart. We the people must listen to this even if the politicians remain deaf. Of course small practices will join together and federate or merge, but that should be done because in their particular area it provides the best patient care. Quality is far too varied and if a larger practice can cover extended hours this is better than bringing in agency GPs for patients.

The RCGP's *Compendium of Evidence* provides information, drawn from national and international sources, relating to the effectiveness and efficiency of general practice. Primary care provides a place to which people can bring a range of problems. They see it as the hub from which they are guided through the health and social care system and facilitates them participating in decisions about their health and healthcare. It potentially builds bridges between personal healthcare and a patient's family and community, and provides opportunities for disease prevention and health promotion, as well as early detection.

GPs care for patients, their carers and families from before birth to after death. They diagnose most illnesses, manage the majority of health problems, promote better health and prevent disease, provide screening programmes, certify sickness and disability, support rehabilitation, monitor and manage a wide range of chronic health conditions, support carers and optimise access to specialist services. Without this function of the personal doctor the hospital services can be used wastefully, even damagingly to the patient. A health service grounded on the general practitioner is going to be less costly than a hospital-based service and the aim should be to provide the maximum amount of care in the community. An Independent Commission on Generalism (2012) concluded that it is vital that the essence of generalism (based in holistic and patient-centred care) is valued and preserved.

The intellectual and contextual framework within which expert generalists operate is as demanding as that of expert specialists; however, it is different in several key parameters. A former president of the RCGP, Iona Heath, said, 'Specialists and GPs, though sometimes perceived as opposites, are inextricably dependent on each other's skills and, crucially, most are keenly aware of the extent of this interdependency.'

In the NHS in England, as mentioned above, more than 300 million consultations take place in general practice per year, which represents 90 per cent of all NHS contacts. The majority of these are undertaken by general practitioners. Although the average patient has 5.3 consultations with their GP every year, only one out of every twenty consultations (5 per cent) results in secondary care referral. Everything else is dealt with in primary care. A whole year's care in general practice costs about one tenth of a day in hospital; a GP receives around £80 per patient per year (UK) for unlimited numbers of consultations.

In America policy-makers and researchers are at last recognising the clinical effectiveness of the family physician, both in providing continuity of care and in the utilisation of the concept of 'medical home', especially for helping patients with co-morbidity. This comes after years of focus in US health policy on single-condition case management – and an emphasis on technological intervention within strictly controlled care pathways, rather than a generalist, integrated or holistic approach.

The need for the whole population to have access to quality general practice has been highlighted by a large USA-based review of all studies published between 1985 and 2005, which quantified the benefits of GPs in reducing health inequalities and improving morbidity. The findings suggested that an increase of one GP per 10,000 population was associated with an average mortality reduction of 5.3 per cent, equivalent to 49 fewer deaths per 100,000 population per year. It would be a supreme irony if, just as the coalition government is dismantling our family doctor service, the US started to build one up.

A series of comparative studies published by the Commonwealth Fund on the performance of twelve international health systems has ranked the United Kingdom consistently high overall, in comparison to others. The United Kingdom's comparative performance shows that it has performed strongly in terms of access to care, equity, effectiveness and patient safety. Yet in just four years this coalition government has thrown so many spanners into the works of general practice that it is now no exaggeration to say that unless the 2012 legislation is repealed and a new course charted for GPs after the general election, by 2020 the family doctor service in England will be unrecognisable and to display the NHS brand on a building in England where GPs are practising could become a palpable fraud.

Money is part of the problem for general practice. It is incredible, as the accountancy firm Deloitte showed in a study published by the RCGP on 2 April 2012, that general practice in England is due to receive just 7.28 per cent of the NHS budget by 2017/18, down from 8.5 per cent when the study was published. Meanwhile, the number of patient consultations in England is estimated to rise to 409 million – up from 340 million in 2012/13. In 2008/9 the number of consultations stood at just under 304 million. The number of consultations in general practice has increased as the population has increased in size and grown older, and as more and more people have multiple conditions. However, the share of funding spent on general practice has been falling since 2005/6. The RCGP warned that the combined forces of rising demand and diminishing funding will have disastrous consequences for safe patient care. The government's 'Plans to Improve Primary Care' is full of un-evidenced assumptions – that IT, home care and schemes to avoid hospital admissions will save money. Good soundbites, such as a named GP for patients over the age of seventy-five, have to be set against the findings of the 'friends and family test', which has shown that seeing the same named GP on every visit does not necessarily improve quality of care. Labour's pledge that patients can book to see a GP within forty-eight hours is a political target, and such targets have been seen in the past to be easily fiddled. Political gimmicks only add to the frustrations and lack of trust towards any government among health professionals and health managers. Changes can and must be made but let them be evidence based, free of gimmickry.

On 5 October 2014 one more public relations announcement by David Cameron was critically exposed in the *Daily Mail*. A flagship scheme to get three million people texting or emailing their blood pressure was to be quietly dropped. So called 'tele-health' was initially claimed to save £1.2 billion. GPs were saying that politicians should concentrate on getting the basics right, rather than obsessing about 'gadgets'. The actual roll-out of the programme was found to be expensive and inefficient. Innovation is welcome but there were much better ways that money could have been spent.

Then on 22 October 2014 a controversial scheme designed to alert tens of thousands of people that they have dementia was announced and written up with a flourish. It was apparently intended to meet targets set by Cameron – again this restless, Blair-like urge to dominate the news at all times and on all issues. GPs had been offered cash for preventive medicine before but here for the first time, responding to the Prime Minister,

NHS England was offering 'cash for diagnoses'. This financial incentive was criticised by a former president of the RCGP as an intellectual and ethical travesty. I wondered how much in-depth consultation had taken place. It soon became apparent that the Alzheimers' Association was supportive, taking the view that the sooner the size of the problem of dementia was established, the easier it would be to plan sufferers' care and work with the people who were or would be caring for them. Cameron had made a promise to increase the diagnosis rate to cover two thirds of the potential number of people suffering from dementia, which he called 'one of the greatest enemies of humanity'. Was this yet another prime ministerial attempt to grab headlines? Had he asked himself whether paying £55 per diagnostic session with a GP was the best use of the money available for dementia patients?

Why had NHS England gone along with this? Their justification was that 'more needs to be done to ensure that people living with dementia are identified so that they can get the tailored care and support they need'. The overall costing was put at £5 million. I remembered the £3 payment I had authorised as Minister of Health for GPs to give contraceptive advice. Paying for advice had been done in the NHS but payment for a diagnosis? As a former neurologist the intellectual and moral issues fascinated me. Then I read a moving article in *The Guardian* by Rose George, whose father developed dementia in his mid-sixties.[102] She mentioned a recently published Research Council report that a quarter of people with dementia hide

---

102 Rose George, 'How not to solve the dementia crisis', *The Guardian*, 28 October 2014.

their symptoms through shame and fear of stigma. They fear diagnosis; they fear losing their friends. George drew attention to a study by Norfolk NHS Trust that found that an Admiral nurse (most easily described as the equivalent of a Macmillan nurse for dementia) saved the NHS £443,593 in a year, in reduced contact with GPs and in the eight mental health bed referrals that were avoided. A likely consequence of what George calls '£55 lollipops' is a substantial increase in referral rates to mental health clinics. But where are the resources going to be found for these people? Already some GPs, only too aware that there is no capacity in their area to help and support these patients, fall short of making the actual diagnosis and go along with what their patient and even the patient's relatives appear to want: to pretend that things are manageable, to avoid confrontation with reality. Again what the NHS is grappling with is an insurmountable problem, but should we not do what makes sense both morally and commercially and what George's mother had campaigned for (eventually successfully) – engage Admiral nurses? In George's father's case, he was admitted to hospital in Wakefield and died on a so-called 'dying adult care pathway' with the disconnection of an intravenous drip. There is here again the unknowing nature of healthcare to be tackled in choosing the least worst solution. Let no one pretend these solutions will be found in the marketplace.

Given all the adverse financial and healthcare trends well known when the coalition government was formed, let alone the nation's financial position after the global crisis of 2008, why did the coalition create the legislative monster of the Health and Social Care Act? It is an important question to resolve. On 13 October it was admitted by the Conservatives that the whole thing had been 'a mistake'. Well, if that is true, why not correct it in 2015? Why is it a mistake to change the Act?

Had a new Coalition government wanted GP commissioning, this could have been done by an administrative decision, making a GP the chair of the then primary care trusts and in all new appointee places putting more family doctors onto the boards. PCT chief executives could have been instructed by the Secretary of State that GP commissioning had to happen. The numbers of PCTs and strategic health authorities could have been reduced, something which did not need legislation and would have happened whoever won the election. A commissioning board could have become a special health authority and the then Co-operation and Competition Panel could have been given a role as an economic regulator, and Monitor left as the regulator of all trusts, not just foundation trusts. Transferring public health to local authorities with financial grants also did not need legislation. The Coalition could then have argued at a stretch that all these changes were evolutionary. But personal aggrandisement meant that Cameron and Clegg had to conjure up landmark changes. Andrew Lansley, to be fair, wanted revolution, not evolution.

As Nicholas Timmins revealed, the department did suggest an alternative route. 'We took [Lansley] through it,' one senior official says, sharply contradicting the view that the department did not try very hard on alternatives. There could have been 'GPs on the board of the PCT; [we could have] abolish[ed] strategic health authorities; [we could have made] the Co-operation and Competition Panel statutory – so you can have one strategic health authority and the competition policy, and we had to do something about the membership of PCTs, and that was it. But

Lansley 'argued that was incremental change. It wasn't nailed down. And the next secretary of state who came along could undo it.' Lansley's view, another says, was that to proceed that way meant

you wouldn't get the benefit of changing everything at once to make this new system work. And the next secretary of state could come along and change it, just as Andy Burnham had come along and said he wanted the NHS to be its own 'preferred provider'. It wouldn't be nailed down.[103]

In No. 10 Cameron's adviser Sean Worth supported revolution.

Indeed there is a story of him literally ripping up a memo from a Downing Street civil servant to the Prime Minister, a memo which highlighted some of the risks in all this, as it was being put into the Prime Minister's red box. And for Oliver Letwin it was all part of a grander reform of government for a post-bureaucratic age.'[104]

Just a few weeks after the 2010 general election, the *Health Service Journal* reported a Health Department official declaring that primary care trusts 'are screwed. If you have got shares in PCTs, I think you should sell. They are under more threat than strategic health authorities.'[105]

On 25 June Lansley told the NHS Confederation in

103 Nicholas Timmins, *Never Again? The Story of the Health and Social Care Act 2012*' (Institute for Government, 2012), p. 58.

104 Ibid.

105 *Health Service Journal*, 10 June 2010.

Liverpool: 'I intend that general practice should take control of commissioning.' Sir David Nicholson, a man who appeared to be living on borrowed time, though he went on to survive longer than expected, said to the same conference that Lansley was 'a man in a hurry', making clear that he wanted the commissioning board operating by April 2012, with GP consortia buying the vast bulk of care. Nicholson outlined the dangers: 70 per cent of big change programmes, he told his audience, 'don't work; they fail – a real possibility in these circumstances'.

> Of the 30 per cent that do work, what are the defining characteristics? Well, the defining characteristic is not the brilliance of the vision. You can have the most fantastic and coherent vision available, but unless the management of change, unless the transition is properly led, you simply won't deliver it.

Nicholson acknowledged that the Treasury was worried about the NHS's financial performance amid all this upheaval. 'But so am I,' he declared. 'I am not going to put financial grip at risk. Never mind the Treasury.'[106]

According to the *Financial Times* of 3 July a meeting of the Coalition Committee with all the most senior coalition members present launched into an unexpected discussion of Lansley's plans with the Health Secretary absent. There were worries about financial control, worries about handing so much power to GPs. And, according to officials, 'the political antennae of Osborne and one or two others began to twitch for the first

---

106 *Financial Times*, 26 June 2010.

time about what all this really meant. I think they thought we'd said no reorganisation of the NHS yet this looks like a massive reorganisation.'

This was in hindsight, according to Timmins,

> a critical moment. The one when it dawned collectively on Conservative ministers, as well as Liberal Democrat Cabinet ministers, that the White Paper was neither Lansley's original plan, which would have involved much less structural upheaval, nor was it the programme for government – again involving a very different structural change to that now being proposed. A thorough pause at this point might have led to revisions.[107]

The pause that was to follow, by contrast, was a PR exercise masterminded by the Prime Minister, whose skills were honed in this art when he was corporate affairs director at Carlton Television. At a private meeting of backbenchers Cameron addressed the problem of presentation but not the politics[108] at a time when sources inside No. 10 were beginning to conclude gloomily that 'there is no policy solution to what is in fact a political problem. We need to reform the politics of this.' Lansley's reaction was: 'Leave this to me to sort out, they all used to work for me.' This was a reference to his time as head of the Conservative Research Department when both Cameron and George Osborne worked for him, along with Steve Hilton, who was with Lansley in Conservative Central

---

107 *Never Again?*, p. 61.

108 *Financial Times*, 15 March 2011.

Office for the 1992 election campaign and was then Cameron's highly unconventional strategy chief. In the end, according to Lansley, the White Paper emerged only a mere week later than planned.[109]

On 9 July, a report from Andrew Porter, the *Daily Telegraph*'s political editor, confirmed that GPs were to be handed some '£60 billion to £80 billion' of the NHS budget in 'the biggest revolution in the NHS since its foundation 60 years ago'. It was, the paper reported, 'a victory for Andrew Lansley' after the Prime Minister had overruled worries from Osborne about handing control of so much NHS cash over to family doctors.[110]

Three days later, just sixty days after the coalition government was formed, the White Paper *Liberating the NHS* was published, without any mandate in terms of a manifesto commitment, from either the Conservatives or the Liberal Democrats, in stark contrast to Labour's NHS mandate in 1945. So useless was the House of Lords in protecting the need for an electoral mandate – one of the few things a revising chamber should regard as paramount – that when the Bill eventually reached it not one amendment was carried that challenged the ideological basis of marketisation, for which there was no enthusiasm and scant evidence that it would either provide better care or cost less.

The Liberal Democrat health minister, Paul Burstow, a former deputy leader of the London Borough of Sutton, now says, according to Timmins, that he and his senior party colleagues in government – Danny Alexander and Nick Clegg – underestimated the 'deep-seated distrust' of the Conservatives

---

109 *Never Again?*, p. 61.
110 Ibid., p. 62.

on health among Liberal Democrat activists, despite the long years the Tories had spent seeking to 'detoxify' the NHS as an issue. And more generally they 'underestimated the extent to which the competition aspects of the white paper would be seen and portrayed'.[111] For NHS staff the Liberal Democrats' acquiescence was every bit as great an electoral betrayal as that which University students felt following the increase in tuition fees.

With the PCTs abolished, it was argued, there was no need for the strategic health authorities (SHAs) to oversee their commissioning role. Another key part of the SHAs' job – overseeing NHS trusts – was set to disappear as all hospitals were intended to become foundation trusts. The Liberal Democrats at least had a manifesto pledge to scrap SHAs. The department had an argument that with huge cuts in management costs being demanded it no longer made sense to have independent SHAs beneath what became NHS England, but they set up twenty bodies under NHS England in 2013 and then started to argue in the autumn of 2014 that they should be reduced by April 2015 to thirteen. A reorganisation on top of a reorganisation.

Eric Pickles, the Secretary of State for Communities and Local Government, when public health was given to local government 'loved the idea', one official said, and declared, 'It's like Christmas.' But

the result of this deal was that what had started out as a big shift of power and accountability within existing structures – transferring the commissioning of care to family doctors

---

111 Ibid.

– suddenly also became a huge structural upheaval. Two entire tiers of NHS management were to be removed. On paper, it had an elegant purity. In practice, it involved a spectacular reorganisation.[112]

The Department of Health was now also faced with £15 billion to £20 billion of efficiency savings, but 'the biggest challenge was trying to get the Secretary of State to focus on the money – the £20 billion and the sheer scale of the financial challenge,' one official said.[113] Lansley's attitude, however, was that 'I am going to do these reforms anyway, irrespective of whether there are any financial issues. I am not going to let the mere matter of the financial context stop me getting on with this because I think they are the right thing to do. And I've thought them all through.'

Another official said, 'We did point out to him that his plans were written before the big financial challenge, and didn't that change things? He completely did not see that at all. He completely ignored it'. Or in the words of another: 'His answer was that "there is never going to be a good time to do this and this will help with the money".'

Lansley was, like Cameron, a politician who had never before been a government minister, though he had been a civil servant and head of the Conservative Research Department. When will we learn? Ministerial apprenticeship is essential.

The *Daily Mail* on 11 July 2013 revealed exactly how costly the reorganisation was from National Audit Office figures,

---

112 Ibid., p. 55.
113 Ibid., p. 56.

which showed that the NHS had spent £435 million between May 2010 and September 2012 on redundancy packages for staff of departments scrapped in the reforms but that more than one fifth of them had found new jobs within the NHS in England with 7,000 vacancies still to be filled. Also 1,341 staff had received payments of more than £100,000 and 173 more than £200,000.

Some GP commissioning enthusiasts were, of course, enthused but others, like Dr Dixon, convinced in theory, were openly worried in practice. 'Only about 5 per cent to 10 per cent of GPs are ready to take on hard budgets to buy care within the next few months,' Dr Dixon said as the White Paper emerged. 'Perhaps 50 per cent will be within 18 months. Others will take longer.' Managerial talent in PCTs – people whom the junior health minister Anne Milton was shortly to describe, to their fury, as bureaucratic 'pen pushers' – needed to be retained.

By February 2011 some 25 per cent of PCTs had been disbanded. A shadow National NHS Commissioning Board was in place by April, before the Bill had even reached its report stage in the House of Commons. There was a drumbeat of control-freakery coming from the Department of Health. In the House of Lords numerous people speaking in favour of the proposals were associated in some ways with them. All declared their interests but everything became very cosy and the blatant ideological basis of the reforms was blanketed out. A self-congratulatory atmosphere prevailed in the Lords, very different from the forensic examination its lawyers sometimes apply.

The size of the GP commissioning consortia, as they were referred to, was always going to be a crucial question. They looked set to vary widely, though many predicted that the NHS tendency to recentralise in difficult times would take effect. For many GPs the responsibilities being thrust upon them were entirely new, and for a large number they were also unwelcome. Many of the best GPs were well aware they lacked the skills, knowledge and experience to fulfil their new roles effectively. More and more GPs sought early retirement, feeling alienated from the language of the marketplace which they had never lived with in the NHS. They were not ready to adopt it at an age when retirement had become an option.

Perhaps the largest proportion of GPs were silent and bewildered, by the changes, offset by a small but very vocal number of activists. Some were driven by concerns for the future of local health needs, others by the opportunities for their own managerial autonomy and authority, and others for the financial advantage that they might gain. One GP, for example, reportedly told an NHS provider: 'I'll commission as little as possible from you, as every penny in your pocket is a penny out of mine'. He was told that this was 'not a great basis for commissioning healthcare'. Meanwhile, Cameron began to talk obsessively about GPs controlling the NHS with no apparent recognition of the realities that they were being squeezed out of the process by accountants and privately run providers.

Lansley started to use the term 'clinical commissioning' rather than 'GP commissioning', something which the Royal College of Physicians and the Academy of Medical Royal Colleges (AMRC) had been pressing for, largely because they thought it would motivate the appointment of some hospital consultants and public health doctors, not just GPs. The Academy argued optimistically that 'this wider involvement will produce more informed and co-ordinated commissioning and better services for patients'. It was claimed that having hospital consultants, not just GPs, would ensure wider clinical leadership and engagement that put PCTs in a poor position relative to many NHS providers.[114] A great upheaval took place, and yet in 2014 many 'GP' consortia still bear remarkable similarities to the old PCTs, with no real patient choice between local practices. An illusion was fostered by politicians of GPs in control – the reality looks as if it will be very different.

A key element much championed by Lansley was the wording in the Bill which allowed for a reduction in the Secretary of State's responsibilities for distributing NHS money, with the all-appointed NHS England, another quango, having the vital task of resource allocation. Sarah Wollaston MP wrote: 'It is one thing to rapidly dismantle the entire middle layer of NHS management but it is completely unrealistic to assume that this vast organisation can be managed by a Commissioning Board in London with nothing in between it and several hundred inexperienced commissioning consortia.'[115]

The unlimited rise of competition and the free choice that was promised was obviously going to make the task of achieving integrated care even more difficult. The AMRC expressed 'serious concerns about possible risks to coherent, equitable healthcare' under the 'any willing provider' model. Despite the rhetoric about greater integration and encouraging cooperation, the demands of the marketplace and the threat of competition

---

114 Nuffield Trust briefing in advance of the debate on standards of care and the commissioning of services in the National Health Service called by Lord Turnberg, 20 March 2011.

115 Quoted in Melissa Kite, 'David Cameron's health reforms risk destroying the NHS, says Tory doctor', *Sunday Telegraph*, 20 March 2011.

complaints were bound to foster fragmentation. The market inherently was for disaggregation of decision making and bound to militate against coherent long-term planning.

The patient–doctor and patient–nurse relationships are personal, intimate and largely unquantifiable. The moment the patient believes that the decisions of doctors and nurses are taken on cost grounds as the result of competitive trading the relationship of trust will alter. The coalition government by crossing over into an external market for health started to embark on a course involving the deepest conflict with age-old values, traditions and concepts of respect and the public good. Health is not a market commodity.

It took time for the health professions to recognise that the proposed external market would change the very basis of vocational care. This change may be on a relatively slow fuse but an explosion will take place when health professionals finally realise that an external market will erode the very art of Hippocratic medicine, which the previous NHS, for all the gibes from the US about 'socialised medicine', never did.

There are also limits to which the NHS can lose its basis in democratic government without also losing the trust of the people who pay for it out of general taxation. The rationing of care in the NHS has broad-based support because it is seen as broadly fair. No other public service retains the same levels of affection and respect, and poll after poll still shows satisfaction with the NHS, despite unprecedented and vicious newspaper criticism.

Community-based care closer to home for people with long-term conditions and needs, developing patient pathways to support self-management of their conditions, and support from care providers beyond the traditional NHS, particularly in hard-to-reach communities, are essential. These providers will often be social entrepreneurs and charities. Yet these desirable developments were current practice before the introduction of an external market.

The Cystic Fibrosis Trust showed how, in a different field, other ways of proceeding are possible. Carefully and after much research they introduced a very worthwhile new payment by results (PbR) development site, with a mandatory national currency for cystic fibrosis care with local prices. The currency comprises a complexity-adjusted yearly banding system, using seven bands of complexity, with no distinction between adults and children. The bandings were derived from clinical information including cystic fibrosis complications and drug requirements. They range from band one, in which patients have the mildest requirement, with outpatient treatment two or three times a year and oral medication, up to a band for patients in the end stage of their illness on intravenous antibiotics for more than 113 days a year. There are many more examples of the adaptive strengths that the NHS has been building up over the years.

The greatest threat to the family doctor service lies in how the clinical commissioning groups (CCGs) see their role. Many have made up their mind that the very concept of one-on-one family doctoring is out of date. They want to continue to pay out vast sums for GP out-of-hours costs to agencies chronically short of staff for night work.

The CCGs, gearing up to take on responsibility for management of GP contracts in 2015, answered a set of questions in September 2014 devised by the *Health Service Journal* (*HSJ*).

The journal came up with a 'CCG barometer', which found that despite a level of confusion and controversy about the policy of inviting CCGs to 'co-commission' general practice, around 180 CCGs have applied for some co-commissioning role. The implications of these findings are profound and these people are unlikely to speak so frankly again since the government was clearly annoyed by the answers the CCGs gave and has been very dismissive of the whole exercise. It had previously not been clear how many wanted to take on delegated-management GP contracts; doing so would give them greater potential to reshape GP services and address poor care, but this was controversial since it would make GPs on CCGs responsible for managing contracts of fellow GPs. The BMA has said it believes CCGs should not be involved in commissioning core GP services. However, 70 per cent of CCG leaders who responded to the barometer survey said they were likely to take on delegated responsibility for management of GP contracts in 2015.

The Tower Hamlets CCG chair, Sam Everington, told *HSJ* that he did not think CCGs should be involved in the direct performance management of practices. He said there was 'a lot of confusion' among commissioners about what co-commissioning might involve. The Norwich CCG chief executive, Jonathan Fagge, said that co-commissioning general practice was appealing to CCGs, but that there was a risk that, if they did not get additional funding to do the work, it might not succeed. Managing GP contracts could also 'entirely change the relationship' between CCGs and their GP members, he said. NHS Clinical Commissioners co-chair Steve Kell agreed that CCGs would need additional management resources and capacity to take on extra commissioning responsibility. Sixty-eight per cent of survey respondents said they expected to take on delegated responsibility for significant specialised services in the next year. NHS England, it was reported, was exploring how it could share responsibility for some of these with CCGs, and whether some should be handed back to CCG control completely, but they had not yet decided.

The *HSJ* CCG barometer also suggests that most clinical commissioning group leaders were lukewarm about the prospect of merging or sharing substantial health and social care responsibilities. Respondents were asked about the policy, being considered by Labour, of making Health and Wellbeing Boards (HWBs) 'systems leaders' for services for people with multiple long-term conditions, disability or frailty. HWBs would set plans for these services, which CCGs would enact. Only 15.6 per cent of respondents said they thought health and care commissioning overall would be improved if that policy was implemented and 29.3 per cent said health and care services would be better integrated. A third said they would personally leave their CCG position and 53.2 per cent said some GP leaders would leave. Just 13.7 per cent said their CCG was likely to give significant NHS commissioning responsibility to local authorities in coming years. Thirty-nine per cent said their CCG was likely to take on social care responsibility. This reveals a very worrying resistance to integration.

Asked to comment about commissioning integration, one respondent said the presence of providers on many HWBs 'would make the difficult decisions on decommissioning services and shifting services more difficult'. Steve Kell said he would be 'extremely concerned about seeing another significant top-down reorganisation and losing that clinical leadership' under the changes being considered by Labour.

The survey by *HSJ* of 109 CCG leaders from 90 CCGs asked them to rate how likely they were to take different approaches, and to explain their own plans. Fifty-seven per cent of survey respondents were accountable officers, 24 per cent chairs and the remainder held other governing body positions. These are, therefore, people who are very likely, if unchecked, to proceed quickly on their contractual models. Nearly three-quarters said they were likely to let large 'integrated' contracts for care for a specified population or populations. Many detailed strategies to create 'accountable care organisations', an approach in which a group of providers are jointly contracted to meet the needs of a defined population. A large number planned 'prime provider' arrangements, in which a single organisation is contracted to oversee and organise services from different providers; and several favoured 'alliance contracting', in which a range of providers are required to work together. All of these would involve a significant overhaul of existing contracts, with the aim of pressing providers to work more closely together.

The survey results suggested that the CCGs' reform plans are focused on services outside hospital, and that many prefer primary or community providers to be in charge of new arrangements. More than 70 per cent said it was likely a significant proportion of GP practices in their area would become part of a single provider organisation. More than 60 per cent were likely to create a 'multi-speciality provider group'-type organisation, based in primary care and incorporating additional specialities and social care services. Less interest was shown in making local hospital trusts the lead provider for integrated care, with more saying this was unlikely than likely. One CCG accountable officer in the south of England said, 'We do not believe the acute trust is the appropriate organisation to lead integrated care for frail elderly people. They may well take on the lead, for example, for the integrated [musculoskeletal] service.' An accountable officer in London said, 'Our ambition is to integrate care between providers using a form of alliance contracting to enable providers to work together as equal partners.' Jonathan Fagge told *HSJ* many commissioners were 'actively exploring different contractual models . . . which move away from the purchasing of activity and start talking about responsibility for the whole population'. He said these moves would involve 'effectively transferring some of that responsibility contractually and financially on to the provider'.

More than 60 per cent said they expected their health economy – both commissioners and providers – to be in overall deficit at the end of 2015/16. Kell, who is also chair of Bassetlaw CCG, warned that the financial environment might impinge on CCGs' ability to bring about longer-term service change. He said, 'At the moment the NHS has to focus each year on balancing the budget without being able to take a longer-term strategic view that is essential. CCGs are going to have to achieve transformation and efficiencies at the same time, which is incredibly difficult.'

In addition Simon Stevens, the chief executive of NHS England, has plans for patients to purchase health and social care services in the community. The frail elderly, disabled children and those with serious mental illness or learning disabilities will from April 2015 be given sums of money to spend as they see fit on health and social care services. This means spending on physiotherapists, even psychotherapy sessions. This is praiseworthy in that it is aimed at keeping these people out of hospital and giving them more independence, but implementation is likely to be time consuming and expensive, competing with other well-tried mechanisms for healthcare. Public relations has its place in any organisation but it can also be diverting. Patients' budgets could be for only a few hundred pounds, but most are thought to be over £1,000. A small number with complex needs will cost much more. Stevens said in June 2014 that 'north of five million patients' could each have a personal combined health and social care budget by 2018, paid for by 'billions' of pounds provided by the NHS and local councils.

This all has to be set against the *HSJ* survey, where 60 per cent of the CCGs' most senior leaders expect to be in overall deficit in 2015/16 and when many of their long-term aims will soon be seen to be mere aspirations set against demands from NHS England to balance their budgets and a lack of investment funding. Who is kidding who – are managers kidding patients, or are politicians kidding managers *and* patients? The political parties are bending over backwards to pretend they can avoid increasing direct taxes to an ever more sceptical electorate, while bringing forth new targets, new policies, all to be financed by one-off schemes that are yet to be proven sources of genuinely new money. One only has to look at the Health Premium Insurance Scheme of 2014/15 and the Public Health Allocation to see how complicated the funding arrangements are becoming. They propose a phased introduction in 2015/16 supported by this September 2014 consultation, all for a modest incentive budget of £5 million.

There can be no doubt that with the virtual ending of competitive tendering as envisaged in the NHS Reinstatement Bill 2015 there will be substantial economies to be made in the whole CCG system and in the huge consultancy fees which are generated by the tendering process. It is too early to be sure where more modest tendering and contract arrangements would best fit in; much will depend on what pattern of health authorities emerge and what is decided over HWBs, issues that have already been touched on. First the primary legislation must be passed and enabling powers under secondary legislation provided for, but to envisage this extraneous organisation continuing unchanged is to remain in the very business model that the NHS must exit from.

Stevens was reported in the *Guardian* on 8 July 2014 as saying, 'We are going to set out the biggest offer to bring health and social care together that there's been since 1948 – a new option for combining them at the level of the individual.' He then outlined his ambitious plan in a speech to council leaders at the Local Government Association's annual conference in Bournemouth. It is very hard to see how such a plan with all its accompanying costs can be rolled out in the fragmented system under the Health and Social Care Act – which Stevens supported – where all hospitals are totally self-governing without any geographical linkage to social care and where his budgetary ambitions have already been in effect vetoed by the Treasury.

As John Lister makes clear in an article on the openDemocracy website, local government should be highly sceptical about many of Stevens's claims.[116] The Netherlands, with better-funded provision in many of these areas than the NHS, on analysing the data from their study of personal budget schemes concluded they were failed experiments. The National Health Confederation in 2011 published reports weighing the merits of such schemes and reported strong concerns from service users, front-line staff and carers. The majority 'expressed suspicion that this policy could destabilise current NHS services replacing them with more for-profit providers'. There were detailed criticisms of high transaction costs and the inadequacy of brokering and monitoring.

Of course such criticisms tend to be dismissed as representing vested interests – reactionary resistance to change by the restless Blairite reformers. But the reformers are guilty too of shying away from the absence of an evidence basis for their claims. I have already praised the work done over the care of cystic fibrosis and I am not averse to continuing with pilot schemes in this whole area. But having spent decades holding regular constituency surgeries I am all too aware from countless individual cases that there are huge difficulties in marrying up, let alone managing, a universal health system alongside a means-tested social security system and means-tested social care. There is talk of the Australian personal budget system but little research evidence accompanies it on its deficiencies and difficulties. The think tank Demos has put forward the 'power of prepaid', arguing that social security benefits and healthcare entitlements can all be put on one card. I am, I admit, hopelessly out of date on the intricacies of the present social security systems but I find such

---

116 John Lister, 'Time to get even with Stevens', openDemocracy website, 11 July 2014.

claims hard to believe. Conscientious MPs know, as do social workers and staff of Citizens Advice Bureaux, that many of the individuals they encounter are depressed , dispirited and unable to sort out what are complex issues without personal help.

Simon Stevens addressed a meeting in Minnesota when he was working in the US and an American business friend of mine heard his presentation. He was surprised at Stevens' enthusiasm for every aspect of the US health care system. Stevens supported the Health and Social Care Bill being pushed through in the UK when in the US and has called for 'vouchers' and 'free hospitals'. He has also expressed the view that EU laws would stymie parts of Andy Burnham's wish for the NHS to be the main provider. He talks in a welcome way of mental health having 'parity of esteem' but fails to admit that NHS England is presiding over far bigger funding cuts in mental health than for acute hospitals. The need is to match rhetoric with reality.

In October 2014 NHS England published a document titled *Five Year Forward View*. It had a surprisingly good press and seeing the battering that the NHS had had in the media over the last few years, that was beneficial. The word 'competition', however, is not mentioned in all its thirty-nine pages. Nor in the sixteen points of the executive summary is the Health and Social Care Act 2012 mentioned. By exclusion the impression is deliberate that the 2012 legislation is a thing of the past, something to be accepted. The Secretary of State for Health as an entity barely exists. Only the shared view of the NHS national leadership. The crisis headlines that thunder down on the NHS every day are ignored. The tone of the report is surprisingly upbeat, to the point at times of unreality. It is clear that the NHS national leadership, as they refer to themselves, have embarked on an expensive public relations exercise between now and the general election to pretend that all is well and that the Cameron/Lansley legislation is not an issue. The *Five Year Forward View* has only a fleeting reference to 'GP-led Commissioning Groups [having] the option of more control over the wider NHS budget'. All this is, to some extent, understandable – they have to be ready as public servants to advise a new government and they should steer clear of party politics in the run-up to a general election. But – and it is a big 'but' – the vacuity of the public relations tone of the document is part of the whole malaise that started to hit the NHS from No. 10 from 2002 and will exist until 2015. It is well illustrated by this extract: 'England is too diverse for a "one size fits all" care model to apply everywhere. But nor is the answer simply to let "a thousand flowers bloom".'

The press, somewhat wooed, no doubt wined and dined, over a suitably long warm-up period prior to publication, seemed for the moment content with what had been pronounced. The document was signed off with the emblems of no fewer than six quangos: the Care Quality Commission, NHS Health Education England, Monitor, NHS England, Public Health England and the Trust Development Authority. It carried all the trappings of a modern commercial company prospectus or annual report. It is the shape and tone of what is to come unless we take back our NHS, restore its values and reinstate its core beliefs.

It is impossible to avoid the conclusion that NHS England management are either deaf or in denial over the fact that the 2012 legislative structure of the NHS is collapsing around itself. We need overall coherent planning for hospital and home care and the present silo structures are not fit for purpose, let alone patients.

Chapter 6

A One-nation NHS

The 999 People's March from Jarrow, which started on 6 August 2014 with the objective of being a national wake-up call to what was happening to the NHS, was yet another reminder to me that we had to channel that protest onto those who would have the power in the next parliament. The mood was well captured by Benedict Cooper, writing in the *New Statesman* blog The Staggers on 9 October:

> I'll admit, there was a part of me that feared what I might find as I headed out to meet the NHS march. I was afraid of stumbling across a sad, aged version of the legendary 1936 Jarrow Crusade it was honouring; a musty heirloom handed down through generations of waning engagement in politics and activism.
>
> I arrived in the centre of Bulwell, on the outer reaches of the city, and joined a small crowd that had already gathered to greet the marchers. By then the dreary clouds were just loosening their grip over the

Midlands sky and the sun was starting to flicker through.

At first it was just a pulsating dot on the horizon. But it kept on coming from around some hidden bend; a trickle, then a stream of people, heading our way.

Pretty soon our little huddle was caught up in a flash flood of bustling colour, sound and energy. Campaigners of all stripes filled the square: unions, healthcare workers, pro-NHS groups, the Labour party, the Green party, Women of the World, bearing the tribal colours of a dozen activist groups, together. My fears disintegrated with the clouds.

It was an electric moment, one that was to be repeated again and again before the march was through. The organisers, an all-women group of NHS campaigners from Darlington nicknamed the 'Darlo Mums', had set off from Jarrow two weeks before, heading all the way to Trafalgar Square to spread the word around the country.

I found Rehana Azam, one of the founders of the march, and as I walked along beside her I asked what had spurred her and the others into action. 'The principles of the NHS aren't intact,' she said. 'We felt it was our civic duty to bring people's attention to what's happening to the NHS. The final straw for us was Clause 119 and the battle for Lewisham before that. If it can happen to one hospital then it can happen to any hospital.'

It's just one of many vivid memories from that strange day in August. I remember the ambiguous mood; a blend of anger and hope. And the people we passed by, showing anything from bemusement to approval to expletive fury at what was unfolding before their eyes. . . .

As the nights draw longer and colder, the health service will be tested, perhaps as never before. The Darlo Mums' crusade might be over, but our NHS has never been more vulnerable, or more in need of people to keep marching for it.

The famous Jarrow March of 1936 had mobilised national concern about unemployment, but it had very little impact on the then Conservative–Liberal coalition's actions to create more jobs. As the 999 marchers walked through the north-east, Yorkshire and the Midlands and then on to the south ending up in Trafalgar Square on 6 September, part of my family was there to greet them and I was only sorry I was unable to be there myself. But how to harness that protest? We had seen how another Conservative–Liberal coalition, which had started in 2010 with so much hope, had fizzled out in mutual recrimination in the run-up to the 2015 general election. How could we make this general election different? How could we hold individual candidates and future MPs to specific pledges to reinstate the National Health Service? How could the spirit of those who had marched in Lewisham, in Tower Hamlets and from Jarrow be captured?

It was a considerable feat of organisation and the numbers marching, though not huge, were a testimony to the widespread concern about the NHS. The trade union movement was a necessary but not sufficient basis for the march. But a full-scale non-party campaign would need the Royal College of Nurses and also the Royal College of Midwives, who took limited strike action for the first time in their history in 2014. Since 2010 nurses have had to tolerate private employment agencies charging as much as £1,794 for a specialist nurse to work a 13½-hour shift in A&E (a little under £133 per hour), when the average hourly rate for an NHS nurse with the equivalent level of training was around £12. Morale and commitment are hard to maintain when NHS staff have had their own salaries so harshly curbed.

The nursing shortage should have been avoided in an NHS that has the potential for national planning to meet likely demand. It is hard to comprehend how nurse training places were cut from 20,829 in 2010 to 17,219 in 2013. Was there a shortage of applicants? No; in 2013, according to Polly Toynbee in *The Guardian*, no fewer than 226,400 applied, a rate of thirteen for every place. Peter Carter for the Royal College of Nursing believes that more than half the applicants were well qualified and with the right attributes. The explanation is that training places were cut to save money. Trusts compete against each other for nurses as well as for other staff and, of course, patients. In 2013 we imported 6,000 trained nurses while the NHS lost more than 4,000. Many British nurses went to the United States, Australia and New Zealand. We go abroad to find nurses in Portugal, Italy, Spain, Romania and the Philippines, and end up with less experienced people, some of whom need training in clinical English. The Quality Care Commission are quite rightly critical in their reporting of insufficient nursing numbers on wards and mistakes made by overworked staff.

Meanwhile the Secretary of State for Health goes for headlines. In the *Daily Mail*: 'Basic errors costing NHS £2.5bn a year', 'Better care could fund 60,000 extra nurses, says Hunt'. Why does he not focus on dealing with recruitment in England so that we no longer have one in five nurses new nurses coming from abroad? Almost half the nurses in NHS England are over forty-five. We are told self-governing foundation trusts are the answer, the evidence daily contradicts it. In the first financial quarter of 2014 such trusts spent £391 million on temporary workers. It is a merry-go-round but there is no merriment in it for anyone. An average patient who develops a bed sore spends twelve more days in hospital, adding £2,500 to their NHS costs. The home birth revolution is in reverse amid a shortage of midwives.

Away from hospitals, preventative or rehabilitative treatments can be undertaken in the community, but these services are also being squeezed. For example, patients recovering from a stroke or a fall need physiotherapy, chiropody, occupational therapy and language therapy, and the key to it all is better overall health planning; hospitals not divorced from the community but joined to the community. Research shows that between 30 and 40 per cent of patients in hospital do not need to be there. In 1973 Sir Keith Joseph and McKinsey gave us district, area and regional health authorities; this structure had at least one tier too many, but crucially it had coterminous boundaries at one level to help hospitals and community health services work more closely with local authority social services. Now we have no such arrangements. The disaggregation of healthcare inherent in the 2012 legislation has ensured that we in England are travelling in the wrong direction, very different from the rest of the UK.

How to nurture a public readiness actually to do something about the health of the nation had concerned me since I and three others started to draft the initial National Health Service

(Amended Duties and Powers) Bill [HL], which I presented to the House of Lords in January 2013 and then again in a slightly expanded version in May 2013 (see Annex A). We tried in July 2014 to persuade those MPs high on the list of the ballot for private member's Bills to build on these for their own Bill. The Liberal Democrat MP Andrew George, who had been a tireless critic of the 2012 legislation, had come first in the ballot but he decided to put forward a Bill on another major subject, the bedroom tax. Then in a conversation with Andy Burnham I suggested a Labour MP might take over my Bill, and Clive Efford fortunately decided to present his Bill to the House of Commons on 21 November 2014. It was given a second reading by 241 votes to 18, using the same title as my Bill (see Annex B). The response to Efford's Bill was made by Allyson Pollock and colleagues (see Annex C).

Efford's Bill is a very welcome addition to the debate on what should replace the 2012 legislation. It is sponsored by a broad range of Labour MPs, including the former Health Secretary Frank Dobson, John Healey, a former shadow health spokesman, Alison Seabeck, MP for Plymouth Moor View, and Dennis Skinner, MP for Bolsover. My provisional analysis, based on the view of Allyson Pollock and her colleagues, is that the most welcome part of the Bill is that which proposes to repeal the 'Competition' sections of the 2012 Health and Social Care Act, which will have the effect of reducing procurement and tendering procedures. This appears in Clause 10, which would repeal Sections 72–80 of the 2012 Act. It would, for example, remove the power to make regulations on procurement, patient choice and competition under Section 75 and, although the Bill does not expressly state that the current regulations made under that section[117] would be revoked, that must be its effect.

The Bill also proposes to give more duties and powers over the NHS to the Secretary of State, compared with the position in the 2012 Health and Social Care Act. These include the duty to arrange the provision of listed services, with powers to delegate this duty to, and to direct, NHS England and CCGs; a general power to direct CCGs and NHS England (as well as NHS trusts and special health authorities, as at present); a power to direct that NHS foundation trusts and NHS trusts cannot raise more than an unspecified percentage of their income from (essentially) private patients – including the power to direct different percentages for different individual trusts; and having to give consent to any merger involving an NHS trust or foundation trust or to their acquisition or disposal of significant property. The Bill does not, however, 're-establish the Secretary of State's legal duty to provide national health services in England', as stated in its long title. This is because Clause 1 repeats the wording in the 2012 Act – 'duty to exercise functions to secure provision' rather than the 'duty to provide or secure provision' in place between 1946 and 2012. Also Clause 3 contains a 'duty to arrange provision' rather than 'a duty to provide' as it was in the 1946 Act, and it drops the long-standing requirement to so do 'throughout England'.

The Bill imposes a duty on the Secretary of State to 'ensure that the health service is a public service which delivers services of a general economic interest and operates on the basis of

---

117 The National Health Service (Procurement, Patient Choice and Competition) (No. 2) Regulations 2013.

social solidarity' (Clause 1(2)(b)). The concept of 'services of general economic interest' derives from Articles 14 and 106(2) of the Treaty on the Functioning of the European Union and Protocol No. 26 of that treaty. The European Commission and member states share competence for these services in so far as member states may seek derogations from EU competition rules subject to the Commission's agreement, which must be sought on a case-by-case basis. By contrast, the Commission has no authority over services of general non-economic interest, which are entirely the responsibility of member states. These terms are not defined and, citing several court cases, the Commission has said that member states 'have considerable discretion when it comes to defining what they regard as services of general economic interest'.[118] It has not been determined whether the NHS is a service of general economic interest. For example, in 2003 the Spanish health service was held by the European Court of Justice not to be such a service. It is essential that the NHS is established as being of general non-economic interest. In 2013 the European Commission stated that 'public hospitals which are an integral part of a national health service and are almost entirely based on the principle of solidarity, funded directly from social security contributions and other state resources, and which provide their services free of charge to affiliated persons on the basis of universal coverage' are an example of 'non-economic activities of a purely social nature'.[119] The Bill does

---

118 European Commission, 'Guide to the Application of the European Rules on State Aid, Public Procurement and the Internal Market to Services of General Economic Interest, and in Particular to Social Services of General Interest', SWD(2013) 53 final/2, Brussels, 29 April 2013.

119 Ibid, p. 33.

not yet appear to provide sufficient changes to challenge EU competition law. It would be helpful if it was explained what the significance is of this wording in Clause 11(b): 'Any person commissioning or providing services for the purpose of the health service shall not for that purpose be an undertaking for the purposes of the Competition Act 1998.'

The Bill would render the NHS a 100 per cent commissioner–provider service. This was not the position before the 2012 Act, and so in this respect the Bill would appear to extend the market in the NHS beyond its previous position under Labour governments – for example, primary care trusts were both providers and commissioners. Yet, as I argue in this book, commissioning remains an unproven policy. As recently as 2010 the Health Select Committee damned it as 'twenty years of costly failure'.[120]

But the Bill leaves in place the wide power of CCGs to commission health services they consider appropriate under Section 3A of the NHS Act 2006, inserted in 2012. This power allows CCGs to operate outside the Secretary of State's duty proposed in Clause 3 (which only replaces Section 3 of the 2006 Act). The power in Clause 5 to direct CCGs about the exercise of their duties and powers could be used to limit the operation of Section 3A, but whether this would happen in practice would depend on the particular government, and it could not be used to take the power away.

The Bill would not reverse the 2012 Act's prospective abolition of NHS trusts and their transformation into foundation trusts

---

120 House of Commons Health Committee, *Commissioning*, Fourth Report, Session 2009/10, HC 268-I, p. 6.

or their takeover by private companies. The 2012 Act requires all NHS trusts to become foundation trusts, and if they cannot they will be merged, closed or taken over by private companies. This would remain the position. This Bill may not be suitable for changing foundation trusts.

With regard to the Transatlantic Trade and Investment Partnership Treaty (TTIP), Clause 14 provides that its ratification shall not cause any legally enforceable procurement or competition obligations to be imposed on any NHS body entering into any arrangement for the provision of health services anywhere in the UK. This very welcome clause does, however, raise a number of questions. Firstly, ratification of a treaty follows signature. It is a step required for a treaty to become binding in international law. Once ratification has occurred, therefore, the obligations referred to would become binding. So Clause 14 may not be sufficient as it appears it might set up a conflict between the UK's international obligations and domestic law and it may turn out that this formulation would not have the effect intended. Clarification is needed as to whether Clause 14 would be effective.

Secondly, the heading of Clause 14 is 'NHS exemptions from proposed [TTIP]'. However, the text of the clause does not exempt the NHS. Rather, its terms are limited to 'procurement or competition obligations to be imposed on any NHS body entering into any arrangement for the provision of health services'. It should therefore be clarified whether it would extend to obligations of the UK (as opposed to obligations of any NHS body), and whether it would apply to both commissioners and providers. The definition of the term 'NHS body' should also be made clear. It should further be explained why it would not extend to other obligations, such as for example the ousting of the jurisdiction of the UK courts, or to the rights of private companies to bid for contracts.

Turning to the procurement regulations mentioned above, these were made under Section 75 of the 2012 Act, which Clive Efford's Bill would repeal. They require commissioners, for example, to advertise new NHS contracts unless the services are only capable of being provided by a single provider. The Bill does not provide that these regulations would be revoked, although the repeal of Section 75 would, I imagine, mean that no future regulations of this type could be made.

Overall for a private member's Bill it is a very commendable effort and offers a rare opportunity for open debate before the 2015 general election. It cannot cover every aspect of NHS reform, for if it did it would be far too long; by comparison in 1973 I tabled a Children's Bill with more than seventy sections, which had much less chance of getting through. This Bill, however, is only sixth in line and it will be very hard to put on the statute book before Parliament is prorogued, which must happen roughly five weeks before the May 2015 general election. Other sympathetic MPs had not been approached such as Andrew George or the Greens' Caroline Lucas. Labour may have preferred to keep a majority of sponsors as Labour MPs, but for the NHS Reinstatement Bill 2015, there will be no exclusions – we aim to build an agreement among all MPs returned in May 2015 that leaving the 2012 legislation unchanged is not a serious option.

Given the rapid deterioration of the NHS, many are now convinced that short emergency legislation will be essential after the May general election. It would be greatly enhanced if there could also be enabling legislation in the same Bill to give a new Secretary of State the power over a period of time to implement without disruption more far-reaching proposals. It is the intention to create a new draft of the NHS Reinstatement Bill 2015 after comments have been received in December from Allyson Pollock and Peter Roderick. This book is my personal comment. Reinstatement legislation we hope will in many ways reinforce Efford's private member's Bill. We will ask MPs and candidates from all parties to put aside narrow partisan interests and commit to supporting such legislation. We intend to seek support from the Royal Colleges, the BMA and the health service unions. In May 2015 the nature of the new parliament may be very different from that which emerged in 2010. Many parties may be needed to build support for any government. No one can be sure what the representation of the Liberal Democrats will be, nor that of the SNP, Plaid Cymru, UKIP and the Green Party, not to mention the MPs from Northern Ireland. All we can do as a non-party organisation is ensure that NHS reinstatement is a major issue at the general election.

Specific legislation around which to campaign, not a mere form of words, will be vital in these circumstances. An all-party structure could be crucial to its success. Of course we do not intend to stop or impede our own supporters from campaigning for their own party to gain a victory or to hold the balance of power. It is the very nature of activist politicians that they will always campaign for their parties to gain the maximum number of seats in Parliament. In the summer of 2014 the Liberal Democrats, who had been surprisingly disciplined for the first four years of the parliament, chose an overt break with the spirit of a coalition where differences are largely papered over and politicians focus on the positive rather than the negative aspects of their partnership. Of course, it is easy to see why they chose this path. They had already blocked the legislation to reduce the number of constituencies from 650 to 600 because of their anger at the Conservatives and in particular David Cameron for actively campaigning to defeat them in the referendum on the alternative vote. But by disassociating themselves in many policy areas from the record of the coalition they were making room for themselves, as they have every right to do, to support changes to the greatest failure of the coalition, namely Lansley and Cameron's 2012 NHS legislation. The desperation of all the other parties to win votes has also been deepened by the ever-greater success of UKIP after it became the largest single British party in the European Parliament following the May 2014 election. By any standard of the emergence of new parties in the past, and after winning two by-elections where Conservative MPs had stepped down to fight and win their former constituency for UKIP, theirs was a considerable achievement, but previous statements on the NHS conflicted considerably with their welcome support for Efford's Bill.

The Scottish independence referendum in September, for a period at least, in a strange way enhanced the appeal in England of UKIP while creating a majority in Scotland to stay in the UK. The very simplicity of coming out of the European Union, now referred to as 'Brexit', has at a time of increasing complexity and disillusionment more attraction. What stands out in contrast to the messiness of EU membership and all the compromises that surround a 28-member organisation like the EU is the danger of leaving. The Scottish voter, it appears, did begin to fear separation and took notice of the warnings of business and the fears of economists. Nevertheless the United Kingdom could well have broken up given the enthusiasm of the young for independence. 'Yes' seemed a solution, 'no' another messy compromise. The campaign against separation was also built on fear, necessarily so from the campaigners' point of view. The last-minute conversion of Cameron, Miliband and Clegg to signing the 'vow' on financial devolution had some effect but it had more than a trace of panic about it. It also failed to settle the issue and gave a fillip afterwards to the SNP increasing in membership. This momentum might not be sustained but it is possible that SNP representation in the Westminster Parliament will increase substantially in 2015. The manner, however, of the UK party leaders' promise extracted by the Scots stimulated a sense in England that the English were being taken for granted with a continued subsidy to the other home nations. Then Cameron raised the suggestion of English MPs voting on English issues. All this populism was ripe for exploitation by UKIP. The victories of the two ex-Conservative MPs, Douglas Carswell in Clacton-on-Sea and Mark Reckless in Rochester & Strood, proved to be a stark warning to all three parties. In the case of Clacton Douglas Carswell won with nearly 60 per cent of the vote and a majority of 12,404. Even in the Heywood & Middleton by-election held around the same time Labour only held their seat by a slim majority of 617 votes over UKIP, down from a 6,000 majority in 2010. In Rochester Mark Reckless gained a majority of 2,920.

In 2015 not only is a hung parliament highly likely, it is also very possible that it will differ from the 2010 result in that a combination of two parties in a coalition may not be enough. As the general election comes nearer the Liberal Democrats will probably revert to their usual position of splitting the difference between the two largest parties, Conservative and Labour, and may therefore take some freedom to disown parts of the 2012 NHS legislation that they in fact voted for. The two largest parties have also in their different ways become ever more disenchanted with a repeat of a 2010-style coalition. While respecting the views of the electorate, if either can get away with the sort of minority government that was undertaken by Labour in 1964–6 and 1974–9, they will.

A Prime Minister after May 2015 will no longer have the right to go to the Queen and ask for a general election after six months has passed, as Harold Wilson did in 1974. Under the Fixed-term Parliaments Act, which will remain on the statute book for at least some months and which Labour have now committed to keeping even if they win an overall majority, a general election can take place before 2020 only if two thirds of the House of Commons votes for a dissolution. It is virtually impossible that either Labour or the Conservatives on their own, even if supported by the smaller parties, could make up the required percentage.

This is a position which the Conservatives plan to exploit, as they appear to believe that no opposition party, in this case Labour, would dare vote against a resolution tabled to call an election, for fear of looking as if they were afraid of losing. That conventional view will, I suspect, not apply for a second hung parliament and in a situation where many combinations of political parties might in theory be able to produce a working majority. A minority government, not necessarily a coalition, can carry on if sufficient MPs guarantee supply for Budgetary matters and votes of confidence. In such a scramble for votes even the Conservatives may be ready to reform the Health and Social Care Act of 2012, particularly if a few of their MPs have sympathy for this position.

Under the rules of the fixed-term legislation, two votes of confidence must be won within a fortnight for the government to fall and another take its place. The same procedure would have to apply before the Queen could agree to a dissolution.

These possible political scenarios have considerable implications for our campaign to reinstate an NHS in England. The Scottish referendum demonstrated that maintaining the NHS as it existed in Scotland was the overwhelming wish of the Scottish people, who did not like the look of what was happening to the NHS in England. Even though health was a devolved power the then Scottish First Minister, Alex Salmond, in the second debate with Alistair Darling was able to raise the spectre of the Scottish NHS being at risk because both the Conservatives and Labour have agreed to marketisation of the NHS in the past. There was no direct connection but Salmond exploited an underlying fear that as the English NHS, with its financing coming from more charging, private finance and privatisation, was moving further and further away from the Scottish NHS, there would be in terms of public expenditure allocations a reduction that would affect the Barnett formula, through which Scotland had had its not inconsiderable subsidy for many decades. Polls conducted after the referendum showed that 52 per cent of Scottish voters had made up their mind which way to vote in 2014 and 18 per cent in the last month of referendum campaigning. The main issues driving 'yes' voters were disaffection with Westminster and concerns about the NHS. Darling did his best to refute Salmond's suggestion on the NHS but he did not sound totally convincing and through his association with the Labour government he was paying a heavy price for its flirtation with marketisation and commercialisation between 2002 and 2007, though never in his own Scottish constituency.

There seemed to be a greater readiness after the Scottish referendum for Labour MPs at Westminster to live up to the promise of repealing the 2012 legislation, demonstrated in Clive Efford's Bill. Hitherto, Labour caution had meant that those who wanted the status quo, like NHS England and its new chief executive, Simon Stevens, were relying on the mantra that 'the last thing the NHS needs is another reorganisation'. There has always been some substance in the concern over any dismantling of legislation and a wish, which I share, not to embark on another major top-down reorganisation. But the day-to-day drip-drip of serious problems that were being thrown up by marketisation and the 2012 legislation has meant that the Lansley–Cameron reforms might not even stand with a majority Conservative government.

The skill will be to build on Efford's Bill and to use enabling powers for the Secretary of State to introduce change only when really necessary and at a pace which the NHS can absorb. The short Efford Bill is a good start but in no way a rival to a larger restitution Bill. It contains essential and very worthwhile reforms and if amended in debate in Parliament and outside will help focus minds. It will also mean that Labour can put it forward to the civil service as part of the pre-election contacts that allow a new Bill to be drafted by skilled parliamentary draftspeople in anticipation that a party currently in opposition may soon be in government.

The first draft of our NHS Reinstatement Bill was opened

for consultation in September 2014. It will be redrafted as already described after the closing date for initial submissions in the middle of December. We had and still have no fixed views on how quickly implementation should proceed. There will be further consultation on the revised Bill and other aspects up until the prorogation of Parliament, expected around the end of April.

It is too early to be definitive about what specific enabling powers are required. But we will make provision for a part of the NHS Reinstatement Bill to have immediate effect such as restoring in full the powers of the Secretary of State. Realistically, given procedures it will be hard to have any new legislation on the statute book by the end of the summer, even with a truncated recess. Other parts will have to be at the discretion of the Secretary of State. For a few months a measure of marketisation and commercialisation will continue. That is a regrettable fact but nevertheless the necessary price we pay for a system of parliamentary governance whose legitimacy stems from the law of the land. During this period there will be some time for consultation and deliberation. It may be possible to move by regulation in some aspects of the legislation but it would be unwise to count on that. Once the legislation has Royal Assent there will be within it the authority for action across a broad field to reinstate the Secretary of State for Health.

The Bill having restated the government's legal duty to provide for a NHS in England, there will have to be discussion and then guidelines issued about the different structure. Enabling powers for the Secretary of State should, I believe, allow any part of England to come forward with plans for a new integrated health authority. Taking into account the desirability of coterminosity with the boundaries for social services. Any continuing NHS trusts and all NHS foundation trusts could be part of such an authority, as will CCGs. Family health services committees might be a way within these boundaries to administer arrangements with GPs, dentists and others; this will need intensive consultation. New contracts for commercial companies would be exceptional and infrequent, issued for services only if the NHS could not fulfil them or where otherwise patients would suffer or where there was a case for having outside cost comparisons which questions the case for elaborate CCG structures.

On 4 October 2014 the reinstatement campaign was formally launched by Allyson Pollock at a fringe meeting at the Liberal Democrats' party conference in Glasgow. Sadly, despite a valiant attempt by people like Dr Charles West, next day the conference arrangement committee refused to accept for debate any motions arguing for changes in the 2012 legislation. This only emphasised the necessity of taking the debate direct to Liberal Democrat candidates across the UK. With our first meeting held in Glasgow, it was a demonstration that there is an English interest in taking the campaign for the reinstatement of the NHS to candidates throughout the UK. For all MPs may be needed to secure a second reading for such a Bill if the 2015 parliament is hung. Hitherto the SNP's Westminster MPs have, as a matter of policy, decided not to vote on most English health matters as it is a devolved power. Now, given that discussions are taking place following the referendum for a new constitutional settlement with Scotland, Wales and Northern Ireland, it could be essential to win the SNP over to being prepared to support NHS reinstatement in England.

If after the May general election there is a minority Labour government, it may on all the parliamentary stages of an NHS Reinstatement Bill be necessary to call on all MPs committed to the concepts of the 1948 NHS and not leave the committee stages only to English MPs. It is not a party political point to point out that amending legislation is unlikely be put forward by a Conservative minority government unless forced to do so by smaller parties. But one could hope that as a result of our campaign some Conservative MPs will be persuaded that at least some corrective legislation might be put forward.

So Conservative candidates and MPs will not be ignored by our campaign. We will engage them in the arguments about what needs to be changed in the 2012 legislation. We know that there were a number of Conservative MPs in the coalition who were very unhappy with important aspects of the NHS legislation. The Campaign for the NHS Reinstatement Bill 2015 will therefore try to persuade Conservative voters that the English NHS needs some restorative legislation. It is probable that fellow Conservatives will be better placed to persuade Conservative MPs to at least abstain on reinstatement legislation. We will also make our case to UKIP, in the hope that they too might be influenced by the strength of our Campaign. In short, all parties will be approached; no candidate or MP will be ignored.

The Bill to reinstate the NHS is not about wholesale restructuring but rather about addressing the current levels of disorganisation and fragmentation within the NHS and abolishing the competitive functions of existing organisations such as Monitor. It is about removing market-driven, fragmented systems, ripe for privatisation and with a large market bureaucracy that has started to divert money from patient care

215

to accountants, lawyers and managers of commercial companies. If not stopped, this trend will gather momentum over time and render the present NHS unrecognisable.

The aim is to build a health system which is coherent, organised, effective and efficient. This will inevitably require some structural changes, but it will establish a system that is more functional and will remove elements of the current structure that are unnecessary, wasteful and costly. These changes, conducted carefully, will be welcomed by the vast majority of NHS clinicians, nurses and managers alike.

Any concern that a NHS Reinstatement Bill would create more upheaval and demoralisation among NHS staff should be allayed by the fact that many clinicians and nurses are calling for an end to the chaos, fragmentation and competition, and a return to more integrated planning structures and systems. Andy Burnham has said that change 'needs to be incremental and evolutionary rather than revolutionary.' He has talked convincingly of a National Health and Social Care Service and of an enhanced role for the Health and Wellbeing Boards (HWBs), which the Liberal Democrats prize as their own creation. Already there are signs that local government is putting influential and concerned councillors on these boards. But the response of CCGs to integration through HWBs, as I have recorded, is so far disappointing.

The design and implementation of structural changes will come from the bottom up and it will be for the Secretary of State to endorse such proposals in response to designs tailored by those who will operate the systems. There will be scope for a greater degree of devolution in the design and delivery of healthcare than hitherto.

There is one immediate action that an incoming Secretary of State could take without waiting for primary legislation, and that is to withdraw the Section 75 regulations and replace them within days with wording taken from the House of Lords debates and used by Earl Howe. It was in the House of Lords that this part of the Health and Social Care Bill could have been amended. A major reason that some amendments were not carried was because these words were trusted. If included belatedly in the regulations they could have an immediate legislative effect and would not run foul of the charge of retrospective legislation. Howe's words were:

> Clinicians are free to commission NHS services in the way that best serves patients' interests and there are no impediments to beneficial co-operation to increase integration, improve quality or reduce inequalities . . . Co-operation for the benefit of patients should not breach competition law. Article 101(3) of the Treaty on the Functioning of the European Union and Section 9 of the Competition Act lay down exemptions which apply if the wider benefits of an agreement outweigh its anti-competitive effects. On an individual basis, we would expect collaborative arrangements whose overall effect was beneficial to patients to meet the criteria in Article 101(3) and Section 9. Competition law would be unlikely to apply to a wide range of NHS services. Some obvious examples are accident and emergency, trauma, critical care, maternity, specialist surgery and many others, particularly in remote or rural areas . . . The NHS often acts to promote social objectives to ensure that patients receive the level of service

that they could not afford or which private companies might not find it profitable to provide. Applying competition law in such contexts makes little sense and such activities are likely to fall outside its scope.[121]

Such changes to the regulations would be feasible since they would stem from the debate and the interpretation given to the wording of primary legislation. Regulations must have their basis in statute law; that is why they are introduced after debate and Royal Assent. The advantage of proceeding along these lines is that, if new regulations were also accompanied by a revised mandate from a new Secretary of State to NHS England, which the Act specifically allows for, many new private and commercial contracts would not be started. It is possible that the large private contractors would challenge such new regulations. Provided the government scrupulously kept away from introducing any retrospective legislation, challenges in court would be unlikely to succeed. As for existing contracts, there is a long tradition in British politics that they cannot be interfered with without damaging confidence in and respect for our democratic system. Though it is highly regrettable, it is likely therefore that some of the contractual negotiations that had started under the previous parliament would have to continue. But the official opposition are perfectly entitled – indeed in my view they have a duty to the potential contractors – to make clear their intention to halt marketisation of the NHS well before the general election, and also make representations to the Cabinet Secretary that no new contracts should go out

121 Hansard, HL Deb, 6 March 2012. vol. 735, col. 690.

in the longer 'purdah' period for a general election held under fixed term legislation.

A consequence of having fixed-term parliaments is that the normal purdah period, whereby new government measures cannot be introduced for 4–5 weeks leading up to prorogation, should be extended to 2–3 months. As mentioned above, we already have the tradition that the official opposition are entitled to consult with officials, in this case in the Department of Health and NHS England, and to ask for draft legislation, such as regulations and new Bills, to be prepared ready for a possible new incoming government. It is in no one's interests that contractual law and practice is damaged during this period. It is important too for those of us who believe, as I do, that the Transatlantic Trade and Investment Partnership should not contain the controversial investor protection clauses (ISDS) that these negotiations are not pushed ahead in any purdah period.

Within foundation trust hospitals and the CCGs, this whole issue of managerial freedom remains very sensitive. For example on land sales, property sales and capital surpluses they currently have unfettered freedom. Foundation trusts have at present some £4 billion sitting on their balance sheets. There is an estimated £7.5 billion worth of unused or underused NHS buildings across England. Monitor is at present working out how to deal with this money. Part of the case for new health authorities is that if they contained within them all trust and foundation hospitals and CCGs as well, they would better represent the interests of the public and where this was done HWBs would be affected. But against that HWBs have the potential, Burnham believes, despite their rather last-minute introduction, to be the preferred vehicle for integration. In truth we cannot yet see the way forward for improving patient representation but directly elected councillors have an opportunity in this framework.) Monitor could be abolished and its functions transferred predominantly to the Care Quality Commission (CQC) and NHS England, as suggested by the Oldham Commission. This has merit but I gather the CQC wants another year or so to absorb all its new responsibilities, which is a reasonable request. Also Monitor, having been quite rightly deprived of all its powers to impose competition, is favoured by Andy Burnham to be granted new powers to promote integration. These are all genuine choices and all new legislation needs to do is to provide the enabling powers necessary for a Secretary of State to act. The Bill could also ensure, as in my second Bill in the Lords, that in future international treaties that would significantly impact NHS could not be signed by ministers without first having obtained legislative approval, a limitation that was introduced in somewhat similar form in 1978 by the Labour government against increasing the power of the European Parliament and which since the 2011 legislation now requires a referendum. As to the size of any new health authorities, in some parts of the country they might mirror district health authorities from the past. But in the post-Scottish referendum period it is appropriate to devolve more power in England than has been contemplated in the past. There would be no one-size-fits-all health authority. For example, it might be decided after the 2016 London mayoral election that a single strategic health authority for London should be established, which would coordinate with social services across all thirty-three boroughs (including the City). There would need to be linkages made: with foundation trust hospitals, of which there are many; with the boroughs, perhaps grouped together with neighbouring boroughs; and with the mayor's office, which would take over the London office of NHS England, which has its own subdivisions. In September 2013 the London Health Commission, chaired by Lord Darzi, was commissioned by Boris Johnson, who rightly observed that London's mayor must be concerned with Londoners' healthcare and should champion better health in the capital. Darzi wrote in his report to the mayor, 'I passionately believe that Britain's local and city governments can become the defining locus for better health.' The Darzi commission talked to every mental health trust in London; this resulted in a city-wide mental health trust and a pledge from all relevant agencies to identify and treat psychosis in half of cases within two weeks of the first signs and symptoms, and all cases within eight weeks. It also called for a £1 billion five-year programme to rebuild or refurbish every general practice in the capital.

In the part of the country I know best there is a case – I put it no higher – for a health authority embracing the geographical counties of Devon and Cornwall. Such a grouping would mirror Devon & Cornwall Police, controversial when it was introduced but now recognised as a sensible size for running an effective police force. The three social service areas, to be integrated with hospitals, would comprise Devon, Cornwall and Plymouth. It would recognise the central role of the Peninsula Medical School, attached to Plymouth University.

Not long ago I found myself at the end of a long stimulating day standing in the very modern Plymouth Medical Centre in the grounds of Derriford Hospital looking up at an old black wooden board with the names in painted gold of the past presidents of the Plymouth Medical Society, one of the oldest in the country. There it was, 1965: John William Morris Owen, my father. All day my mind had been focused on one subject, how to grapple with the legislative framework for integrating the NHS and local authority social services. How to bridge the care gaps between hospitals and homes, homes and hospitals. I had been reading on the morning train from London about the integration of health care and then in the afternoon talked with experts from Torbay and Southern Devon Health and Care NHS Trust and South Devon Healthcare NHS Foundation Trust, who more than anywhere else in the country have created a much-admired model of integration. Finally, here in the city of Plymouth, where I was born and for which I am the longest-serving MP, I was talking to a wide variety of people who lived daily with the problems of integration. I remained puzzled. My sister was with me, a former psychiatric social worker in the city, and some of the older people I met had known my mother, an alderman of Devon County Council and for many years chairman of its health committee with a special interest in the mentally disadvantaged. I stress this family history because it has advantages to have deep roots when considering radical change and I had been helped by being the Labour candidate for Torrington in north Devon from 1962 to 1964.

Thinking this might be the last time I might speak to the Plymouth Medical Society I looked at the board before leaving and seeing my father's name again I suddenly could hear his oft-repeated and favourite classical adage: the oxymoron 'Festina Lente', picked up in Rome in 1944 when in charge of a convalescent hospital. 'Hasten Slowly' is not a bad guide to integration, for there has to be a sense of urgency but also the changes in English healthcare today have to be evolutionary. There has to be as early as possible a restoration of the powers of the Secretary of State for Health, and NHS England would best be made a special health authority (SHA) and no longer a quango. At the same time the worst elements of marketisation must be surgically excised from the Health and Social Care Act 2012. But as so often in healthcare there are the unknown aspects of integration and on this we need to move only with deliberation.

Andy Burnham has talked of a 'ten-year journey', saying that people should 'embrace [integration] at a pace that feels right given the nature of the arrangements that they have at a local level'. However, he has also said, 'The quicker you embrace the notion of a single service and a single budget, the quicker you will be placing your health economy on a path to sustainability. The longer people stick in silos, and argue, I would guess that will increase not diminish the funding problem.'

Torquay, Paignton and Brixham were, from the start, a community NHS provider which in 2005 accepted delegated responsibility for all adult social care from Torbay unitary local authority and their social care was very clearly within the main acute hospital catchment area. In 2011 the community provider extended from Torbay to provide adult community health services over a wider area, reaching from Dawlish to Tavistock with extended responsibilities taking in an additional arc around Derriford Teaching Hospital, east of the river Tamar outside the Plymouth city boundary. The social care requirements of this part of the community align to Devon County Council but with close working relations to ensure a patients' journey is streamlined and seamless in its delivery. That organisation became Torbay and Southern Devon Health and Care NHS Trust and is now progressing on a further journey to merge with South Devon Healthcare NHS Foundation Trust (the local acute provider organisation), whereupon it became an integrated care organisation. This geographical area includes eleven community hospitals, some very small. Working relations with the community and acute trusts are close, with a constant wish to think afresh, to adopt and try new ideas. Monitor is at present assessing where to go next but few doubt the foundation trust will take over the care trust and there will then be a single employer. The fictional Mrs Smith, created as a composite model to guide police, has been working out well.

The catchment area of the Plymouth Foundation Trust includes Tavistock, part of Ivybridge and Newton Ferrers, and while this area is being made to work, one wonders whether it should come under Plymouth. A similar area on the Cornish side of the Tamar coming under Plymouth would make sense. An inhibiting factor may be Devon County Council's longstanding reluctance to see an expansion of Plymouth's city boundaries, something they share with Cornwall. Changes in constituency boundaries, when they go outside a city boundary, almost always lead to an enlargement of the city. Local authorities fear, therefore, boundary adjustments in services for fear they presage city boundary changes. There is the additional legacy of the decision of Exeter University to break away from the joint Peninsula Medical School with Plymouth University, which did not improve relations.

The acute hospitals in Exeter and Barnstaple will soon have joint budgets with care trusts but whether there will be an overall health authority for Devon, Plymouth, Torbay and Cornwall is not yet clear. At the level of policing such an arrangement works for the two counties and the city remarkably well, with their three local authorities recognising the need for their police professionals to combine. That this has been done so successfully against many dire predictions about rural and urban needs being so different when it was brought in by Home Secretary Roy Jenkins in the 1960s is encouraging. Whether such a pattern will speed up or delay health integration is a fundamental question. Will Cornish objections win out, as has happened so often in the past?

A Peninsula Health Authority of Cornwall and Plymouth built around the thriving medical school might make most sense since already the students spend much of their time gaining practical experience in Cornwall and there has been a broad acceptance that most specialised treatments have to be located in Plymouth.

Plymouth is a Cromwellian city and was surrounded by Royalists. It has always been tightly encircled by nature: the granite of Dartmoor to the north and north east, the river Tamar to the west separating Plymothians from the independent-minded Celts in Cornwall, and the sea of Plymouth Hoe to the south. This makes it hard to integrate the city, but its university, communication links and size make it essential to do so. But there is no support for a West Country region beloved by Whitehall with Bristol as its centre.

We must recognise in England that we are overcentralised. London has too great a dominance in England, but at the same time its position as a global city in competition with New York to be the most important city in the world is not fully acknowledged. A recognition of this must lead to greater self-governance, and part of that could include the emergence of a unique city-wide health authority.

I have no English blood in my veins: both my parents were Welsh though with a touch of Irish and Austrian blood. In the UK context I feel Welsh. I stress this while emphasising that part of me thinks like a Londoner, where I have lived since 1959. When on the board of governors of Charing Cross Hospital in 1967 as an MP a new building in Fulham away from its original site opposite Charing Cross railway was planned. Over many decades there were four regional health authorities for all of London, like quadrants in a cake extending beyond the then Greater London Council area. I was never happy with this arrangement when Minister of Health. Now London has become the only example of regional government in England and since it took on London transport the elected mayor's office has shown itself capable of handling big strategic questions. With the new mood of devolution in England, London must be the prime candidate for a devolved health authority with its own partial source of funding. Its relationship in the overall planning of health for the UK and for England should be directly with the Secretary of State for Health, not NHS England, and if made an SHA it would interface with the rest of England. The predominance of London in the planning of health has often led to solutions that are not always applicable in the provinces.

A letter in London's *Evening Standard* on 3 November 2014 called on 'national politicians to commit in their manifestos to freeing London City-wide and local government and granting the capital the full range of property taxes as set out in the London Finance Commission'. It went on to list areas for giving London more power over policy and included 'social care and health'. The signatories are influential: three Labour MPs who are widely believed to want to stand for mayor of London in 2016, a present deputy mayor and Sir Stephen O'Brien of Barts Health NHS Trust. An editorial in the same paper headlined 'Give the capital power to control its future' shows that this campaign will gain strength. In particular the specific prohibition from spending on health would have to change and a new relationship negotiated with the thirty-two London boroughs. Vernon Bogdanor, Professor of Government at King's College, London, has been correct to point out that 'if power was to seep upwards from the Boroughs to the Mayor, that would be centralisation, not decentralisation'.[122] But, as he also admits, devolution has meant, with more financial independence, centralisation and a weakening of local government.

Another part of England where the solutions for integration may be different is the north-west. When I was chancellor of Liverpool University between 1996 and 2009 I began to see the strengths of north-west England, with the revival of Liverpool as a city and its inter-relationship with Manchester. I saw the influence of a university and a powerful medical school – very different from London, very different from the West Country. Here the possibilities lie between devolution and decentralisation and include allowing a number of big city-wide strategic health authorities. There is a difficult choice as to whether they should come under NHS England or the Secretary of State. Perhaps size will be the determining factor and the extent to which there is more, if not total, self-financing.

All this demonstrates the need for enabling primary

---

122 *London Evening Standard*, 3 November 2014.

legislation in the NHS Reinstatement Bill 2015 to give the Secretary of State the authority to act over time without needing specific legislation. Within such a variegated pattern of health care in England there is an even greater reason to re-establish central authority of the state's infrastructure of care services. One only has to look at the Ebola virus crisis in west Africa to realise the challenge that could come our way. I encountered the first case of Ebola in 1976 when Minister and, as I remember, we relied heavily on the skills and the facilities of Porton Down in Wiltshire, which was then a military establishment. There has to be a UK responsibility for some aspects of public health, which was acknowledged even in the legislation for Scottish devolution. Within England there must also be central responsibility. It is essential that we have and retain the right skill mix, scientifically and medically, and are able to fully develop its distribution within a training structure that is not dependent on the vagaries of the finance-driven agendas of foundation trust chief executives nor even the agendas of local education and training boards.

There have been increasing concerns about the state of pathology services since the Carter review[123] started off its reconfiguration in 2008 with the support of the Royal College of Pathologists. There has, however, been variable implementation and there is no doubt that much of this good work has been derailed by the Health and Social Care Act 2012's so-called cost efficiencies and the establishment of CCGs. NHS England

---

[123] *Report of the Second Phase of the Review of NHS Pathology Chaired by Lord Carter of Coles*, available at http://www.rcpath.org/Resources/RCPath/Migrated%20Resources/Documents/R/Review_Report_final_proof08.pdf (accessed 15 November 2014).

made the wrong choice in saying that the commissioning of pathology was a local responsibility and this needs to be quickly changed since it is closing any chance of a unified view of pathology services in England as everyone seeks to protect their own budgets. It is a tragedy that we are coming close to the point of having no national view of demand/need, workforce/ capacity and built-in flexibility. There is no contradiction here in wanting on pathology services and other key aspects greater centralisation. An NHS in England which is ready to become more decentralised and embrace devolution has an even greater need than before for a national pathology service, just as I explained in Chapter 4 we have to build up NHS Blood and Transplant as an SHA.

NHS care in England is under the present system commissioned and delivered through 240 different provider trusts, 211 clinical commissioning groups and tens of thousands of GPs. The providers plead for more independence, more autonomy as the system collapses around them. There is much talk of integration between hospital and home, but far too little about integration between hospital and hospital. We have created silo after silo over the last 15 years. It is to me, at least, reminiscent of the silos created in the international financial service industry over some of the same period and which precipitated the global economic crisis of 2008 that is still with us. Silo structures create a silo mentality. That is happening in the NHS and it has to be addressed.

I expect many different patterns will evolve across England as we change the system and if they are carefully monitored centrally we can learn and adapt from the experience. In 1968 I edited a book called *The Unified Health Service*, and as discussed later, we put forward the suggestion then as to how a structure could be developed for the health services which would link health administration to both local and central government. The solution we believed then, and I still do so today, was based on having at some level a linkage across the same physical boundaries for health as for local government. Here there is the potential to build on the Health and Wellbeing Boards and possibly see smaller and fewer CCGs becoming their executive arm within an overall single authority. At the start of the twenty-first century, unwisely, trust and foundation trust hospitals were established, breaking their developing integration with local social services. We are now having to start again after the fact, which is never easy. Nevertheless we have to break down the isolation, both geographic and on some issues, while retaining a fair measure of managerial independence for foundation trusts. The balance is not right at present and independence too often runs counter to integration.

The Torbay experiment shows that isolation, geographical and managerial, can be overcome but its solution, a takeover by a single acute foundation trust of the community care trust, will not be appropriate in all cases, particularly in a large city authority where there are many acute trusts and in some a number of social service authorities. Torbay has shown a way to a single health budget and single employer but it is not the only way.

There are new patterns of care developing within general practice that need to be encouraged. GPs are innovating already, recognising that a generally healthy person can be managed by telephone and email, whereas an older person and people with diabetes, dementia or lung diseases need more personal attention.

Not just larger GP practices but specialist practices or specific GP lists are emerging within a wider network of practices dedicated to more specialised care at home. A report by the Nuffield Trust, *Is General Practice in Crisis?*, states: 'These practices or lists could be supported by a team of GPs, specialists such as geriatricians, psychiatrists and rural physicians, pharmacists, nurses, social workers and others.'

An interesting article appeared in the *Daily Mail* of 19 November 2014 by J. Merion Thomas, an NHS surgeon arguing with obvious passion for the integration of general practice and hospitals in which highly trained nurses would play a 'pivotal role'. In it he said:

> We do not need more GPs. What we need is a new model for the provision of primary care, one based on the integration of general practice and hospitals, in which highly trained nurses play a pivotal role.
>
> Consider asthma, a complex illness affecting 5.4 million people in the UK and resulting in 1,200 deaths annually, with treatment costs exceeding £1 billion. Imagine a service where specialist nurses work partly in hospital chest units and partly in GP surgeries. Expertise would be maintained and patients would have ready access to medical investigations not normally available in general practice.
>
> Imagine nurses expertly trained in caring for the elderly who have detailed knowledge of the care services available, who are based in hospitals but work in the community, with responsibility for regular home visits. Now apply that model to the care of diabetes, to palliative care and so on – and the problem of a lack of access to our GPs is solved.

Another dimension is becoming more involved in the process of integration, part of a trend towards more GPs working as salaried employees, as part-time workers and employing practice nurses, and fewer holding their own contracts. In 2014 some 66 per cent held their own contracts, down from 79 per cent in 2006. If we heard a little less from the present government about GPs' role in commissioning, which they exaggerate, and a little more about resources for retaining and retraining GPs, and for strengthening primary care, patient care could improve. It is possible to achieve a new balance between hospital, social work and GPs. Integration has to involve them all.

A report on whole-person care, *One Person, One Team, One System*, from an independent commission chaired by Sir John Oldham, contains many practical realistic wisdoms. If we 'hasten slowly' structural change and efficiency can walk hand in hand with the best interests of patients, but we should be wary of the predictions of substantive savings to come from integration and keeping patients at home and out of hospital. Savings can be made but their size can and often is being exaggerated. Conflicting interests have to be weighed, economies over convenience in terms of hospital stays. But there are simple innovations that can have a surprising effect. The Royal Liverpool University Hospital saved £11.5 million by switching from twice-weekly to twice-daily ward rounds by consultants, because that halved the length of stay and cut bed occupancy by 7.6 per cent. Replicating that in other hospitals could save tens of millions of pounds, according to the Academy of Medical Royal Colleges, which also believes that as much as £2.3 billion a year is needlessly spent on X-rays, drugs and treatments. But if the precautionary instinct is curbed, then if mistakes later appear, there has to be less vindictive comment and more recognition of the difficult choices between cost and care. In this the National Institute for Health and Care Excellence, NICE, has a key role to play in keeping us all, politicians and physicians, to evidence-based decisions. Any publicly provided national health service has to face up to reassessing for example the forty cancer drugs and ten possible new additions being paid for out of the government's Cancer Drugs Fund. Some believe NICE should take its techniques into assessing home care options.

This self-questioning within the medical profession is to be encouraged at every point in its decision-making. But it must be underpinned and accompanied by a greater public readiness to accept mistaken judgements made in good faith. Parliament must take the lead here and not follow every inquiry into mistakes or scandals with new, demanding and costly safeguards. It means a readiness from all of us to live with the risks inherent in the practice of medicine. One of the past moments I reflect on often in my career was a Cabinet subcommittee meeting I attended representing the then Department of Health and Social Security in probably 1975–6 when the issue was whether to adopt 'no-fault insurance'. Very narrowly on a vote we who wanted it introduced lost and it was noticeable that the lawyers on the committee were the most strident in their opposition. This was a moment when it could have been easily introduced; affection for the NHS was strong, patient complaints to a hospital were not infrequently accompanied by a rider that they did not want compensation but just hoped their complaint would lead to the same mistake not happening again. Whatever the multifarious reasons for such a change of attitude we have lost much of that intrinsic goodwill. New Zealand has such an insurance scheme based on the 'no fault' principle in dealing with medical harm, where it is regarded as a success. What such a scheme does is to quieten down, the demands for financial compensation – it can never eradicate them entirely – and the ever-greater sums of money awarded for malpractice. This is a huge and ever rising cost to the NHS in the UK.

In 2010 Scottish Government Social Research published a fascinating in-depth review of this whole issue, drawing on New Zealand's experience, called *No-fault Compensation Schemes for Medical Injury*. It found in surveys considerable public interest and support and expressed interest in taking the issue further. I very much hope Scotland introduces it and paves the way for a similar scheme for England, Wales and Northern Ireland.

There are many reasons why this variegated pattern might, I suggest, become more appropriate. Extensive devolution to Scotland has triggered a new wish to see greater decentralisation in England. 'The genie is out of the bottle,' says Sir Richard Leese, leader of Manchester City Council. 'Devolution' was once a word seldom heard in Manchester, but Mancunians now see advantages in what their Celtic friends already enjoy. There has never been great enthusiasm for English regional government outside Westminster think tanks and when the north-east in a referendum rejected such a body it was signing a death knell for democratic regionalism for England. We in the West Country never accepted governance from Bristol. But the success of elected mayors and a new high standing which many big cities like Birmingham have earned while rejecting the mayoral model give confidence that the great metropolitan corporations that built and governed their cities in decades past with distinction and established a recognisable character can and should have a role in health. It is also likely that these cities, where there are at present a substantial number of foundation trusts, teaching hospitals and highly specialised units, would find it easier than some smaller ones to accept local government strategic planning that builds on those traditions. Such planning authorities now have proven records for providing good governance. Outside the big cities, the large county councils that uphold rural traditions and are also responsible for social services may in some cases decide they do not wish to link with neighbouring counties. The case for named health authorities of a widely variable size can and should contribute to a varied devolved pattern of healthcare in England, in some cases it may be that NHS England is not needed to exercise overall strategic supervision for large health authorities. Many of these issues that I highlight are for detailed discussion. My ideas carry no more or less significance than that. They are not the considered views of the Campaign for the NHS Reinstatement Bill 2015.

That the 2012 legislation should be preserved when it is an acknowledged failure is absurd. Progressive planned structural changes, tying together social care in local authorities and trust and foundation hospitals, are practical and sensible. We all know that it is necessary for standards of care, both at home and in specially designed residential homes, particularly for the elderly and for the disabled, whether privately or publicly run, to improve and for fewer such people to be cared for in our hospitals. For that transition to take place many things have to change. The Francis report on the Mid-Staffordshire NHS Foundation Trust has many lessons for us all, particularly its central recommendation 'that a fundamental cultural change is needed'. For those politicians who pinned so much hope on the free-standing independent NHS foundation trusts there is a warning. Paragraphs 4.71–4.80 demonstrate that Mid-Staffordshire was authorised as justifying foundation status because of pressure from No. 10 between December 2006 and June 2007. Without such pressure the Department of Health would have been very unlikely to have authorised foundation status for that hospital. Colchester General Hospital may be another scandal.

The so-called 'private patient cap' will inevitably be controversial, but Clive Efford MP was wise to legislate for the fixing of a percentage to be made with flexibility by the Secretary of State after due consideration. Under the Labour government NHS trusts had no cap on how much private patient income they could earn, and it was left to each individual hospital to decide to what extent it undertook non-NHS work, whereas in foundation trusts private patient income was limited to the percentage they received at the time that legislation was passed. It is always claimed that every penny of private income is to be used to improve NHS patients' services and care. In 2009 Unison had won a court case overturning the interpretation that Monitor had developed on capping as being too narrow and one should look at the 'reality' of where the income had come from.[124] So as a consequence a change in the legislation was probably inevitable, but not the actual new amendment, which placed the cap at 49 per cent of total operating revenue of any trust's income, a level far above that which even the Royal Marsden Hospital, an international centre for oncology, had yet reached. This percentage will have to be reduced but in fixing it

---

124 *Financial Times*, 10 December 2009.

there is a danger of igniting the old private–public debate. On 4 September 2014 the *Financial Times* reported that in 2013/14 non-NHS income made up less than 1.6 per cent of the total operating income for the foundation trust sector and private patient income stood at 0.92 per cent, which was only a small rise on the year before. Hospitals showing a dramatic increase in revenues from private patients include Great Ormond Street, which has seen a 34 per cent increase from the financial year 2010 to 2013, and its management needs to watch this if it is to retain its huge public support.

The 1948 legislation allowed for public and private medicine to coexist: that was one of Aneurin Bevan's essential compromises. By contrast the 2012 legislation has far more important flaws and ideological obsessions than using it as a vehicle to challenge the 1948 consensus. It would be a politically costly diversion to go into battle over the role of private practice. The Bevan compromise that lasted even through the Thatcher years should continue. Everyone is entitled to spend their after-tax income on private healthcare but they now have no tax concessions subsidising their private insurance. The same rule applies to education and has been judged a basic human right. Re-establishing a variegated pattern of health authorities with a wider legitimacy and covering a larger area of NHS activity than trust or foundation trust hospitals will be better able to judge how to handle the all-important interface between private and public medicine when conducted in NHS buildings. I was Minister of Health when this issue inflamed the NHS in the mid-1970s. There was a strong case for geographical separation. But there was also a case for consultants working in the same place. That argument should not be repeated. It damaged the

NHS and I for one have no wish to return the NHS to that debate. But one thing has become utterly clear – the structure and management of trust hospitals, whether foundation or not, is too narrow a context in which to make such determinations. With overall guidance from the Secretary of State these issues are best dealt with flexibly in a wider health and care setting.

For reasons of openness and transparency I should declare my own position. When I became chairman of a public company in the UK in 1995 I took up, as every other employee did, private health insurance with BUPA. I maintain it to this day as I am still chairman of Europe Steel, although it is now a wholly owned subsidiary of the Russian company Metalloinvest. My present premium is £6,931, which is declared as an employee's benefit to the Inland Revenue. I have used it for elective surgery, such as hernia operations and prostate biopsies, and for occasional consultations, all in clearly defined private facilities outside the NHS. Alongside this I remain, as do the vast majority of people with medical insurance, with a general practice under the NHS that I have been part of since 1965.

On 6 September 2014 the *Daily Mail* found, following Freedom of Information requests, that out of ninety-two hospitals in England, twenty-nine said that they did allow patients to self-fund treatments. Patients pay for a procedure as a one-off, not through insurance, and have it at their local hospital, claiming that it is just as if it was being carried out by the NHS. Guide prices are issued. The My Choice service at Warrington and Halton hospitals in Cheshire began in 2011/12 with forty-one cases, rising to 382 in 2013/14. Similarly in Reading a figure of 455 cases in 2011/12 rose to 1,747 in 2013/14. It represents a two-tier NHS service: fast with less waiting for some and a slower, more limited service for others. This development needs watching carefully.

The massive issue facing the NHS in the next parliament is finance. The *Financial Times* in association with the Nuffield Foundation reported on 6 October 2014 that, based on an analysis of millions of records showing that hospital admissions will have grown by two million or 16 per cent over the seven years to 2015, an ageing and growing population will need an additional 6.2 million overnight stays in hospital by 2022, the equivalent of twenty-two more hospitals. This demand alone could be responsible for a quarter of the £30 billion funding gap predicted by the *Five Year Forward View*, announced by Simon Stevens in October 2014 (see below). The combination of deep cuts in social services funding, because of restrictions on local authority budgets, and a widespread failure to invest in intermediate care facilities, makes it hard to discharge patients safely. This has meant that progress on cutting the time patients stay in hospital stopped altogether in 2012/13.

The fragmented, competitive system of foundation trust hospitals will not work effectively everywhere. Take the dispute between the Brompton Hospital and the Royal Marsden Hospital, both in west London. One wanted to sell off NHS buildings, replace them with expensive flats and use the capital; the other wanted to buy the NHS buildings and use them. Neither could persuade the other and NHS England was powerless to intervene, as was the Secretary of State. They were left appealing to their local government's help in determining the issue. What a mess. The restoration of planned hospital and community care that we experienced and progressively improved under various health authorities over the past decades has to be revisited.

The UK's National Health Service has many substantial merits. The US-based Commonwealth Fund surveyed healthcare services in eleven advanced countries, seven European states, the US, Canada, Australia and New Zealand. In its many measures, based mainly on patients' opinions, it found the UK to be at or close to the top of almost all its indicators and yet UK health spending per head was the second lowest in the survey.

There is one very worrying statistic, however, from the World Health Organization, based on medical outcomes judged by reference to avoidable mortality, infant mortality and healthy life expectancy at age sixty. In 'mortality amenable to healthcare' and measuring excess deaths attributable to smoking, drinking, obesity, hypertension and preventable diabetes, the UK and the US come out far worse than the other nine countries and while infant mortality has fallen dramatically worldwide the UK does not come out well and the US has the poorest record of advanced countries. One only has to look at that list to realise that we are not doing anywhere near enough in preventive terms and the food industry, not just the tobacco industry, need far tougher controls. That sugar levels should be so high in drinks and foods designed to be bought and consumed by children is part of the explanation for the epidemic of obesity that has been tolerated within the UK for too long. It is no comfort that the survey shows that the US spends a much greater proportion of its national income than other developed countries without any clear impact on the overall quality of medical care.[125] But it is a warning not to ape the US healthcare model. That

---

125 John Kay, 'The best health system is not always the one that keeps us alive', *Financial Times*, 24 June 2014.

is why Stevens as chief executive of NHS England is right to stress prevention, but he will have to challenge the food and pharmaceutical industry more than is even contemplated in the US. The market-based insurance health care model in the US on the basis of hard evidence is not one to be reproduced in the UK.

The Campaign for the NHS Reinstatement Bill 2015 will without exaggeration draw attention to the fact that the UK has one of the most cost-effective health systems in the world, which has allowed successive governments to spend far less on health than other comparable countries. It is sheer escapism to blame the NHS for the lack of funds allocated to it. In recent years the *Financial Times* has pointed out that NHS net savings from combined efficiency savings and demand management have peaked at about 2 per cent, but close to a third of that has come from a partial freeze in NHS pay, which is not sustainable. Opinion polls show one area where the NHS is unique: the British people are ready to pay more tax to improve it, provided that that tax is a general health tax specifically earmarked for the NHS. Now establishing a new earmarked health tax takes time and it is clear already in the way that the three main political parties are coming up with pledges of spending for specific purposes covered by particular selective taxes, driven by focus group research, that this, not a new earmarked health tax, is how they intend to garner votes. If they will not propose a wholly new hypothecated health tax we need to champion other sources of money for the health service. With the introduction of the lottery fund that source is pre-empted but many in the arts and heritage fields have benefited from that innovation. Why not try another innovation and create an NHS Investment Trust?

The consequences of the Private Finance Initiative with the expert views of Allyson Pollock, who heads the Campaign for the NHS Reinstatement Bill 2015, are discussed in Chapter 3. PFI is a very expensive way of borrowing money for the NHS: annual repayments will cost huge sums of money for the next thirty to sixty years.[126] In all, the Department of Health is liable for £79.2 billion of repayments on total PFI capital costs.[127] The current trajectory of repayments is causing significant and lasting damage to trusts and foundation trusts throughout the country, closing key services and threatening the existence of hospitals. This pressure must be relieved and, in the prevailing fiscal climate, will require revenue streams that do not significantly encumber deficit reduction plans nor harm other essential services. At the heart of any successful effort must be the centralisation of PFI contracts, allowing for application of increased bargaining power in the renegotiation of terms, which is essential in handling the PFI problem. In doing so, it must be asked who is best positioned to support hospitals in contract centralisation and repayment while able to exercise significant bargaining power over the terms of any contract renegotiation and apply the expertise of finance industry specialists. Neither the Treasury nor the NHS is for a variety of reasons well placed to accept this role.

As such, there is a case for dealing with the PFI problem in an imaginative way that would at the same time make a

---

126 Allyson Pollock and David Price, 'PFI and the National Health Service in England', available at http://www.allysonpollock.com/wp-content/uploads/2013/09/AP_2013_Pollock_PFILewisham.pdf (accessed 15 November 2014).

127 Denis Campbell, James Ball and Simon Rogers, 'PFI will ultimately cost £300bn', *The Guardian*, 5 July 2012.

major inroad into the NHS's current financial difficulties. A charitable 'NHS Investment Fund' could be established with its remit agreed with the Charity Commissioners and so enjoy the status and exemptions associated with such an entity. It would be in no way involved with the provision of services. It would initially be charged with handling all aspects of existing and future PFI agreements solely within the NHS. It would be hoped that over time, primarily through contract renegotiation, it could substantially reduce the overall cost of PFI borrowing. Immediately the cost to the NHS bodies connected to PFI agreements would be transferred to the NHS Investment Fund, which would pay the private companies. This centralisation would allow for the rationalisation of PFI contracts and increase bargaining power in their renegotiation. Crucially, the fund would enjoy autonomy, being empowered by a mandate to relieve financial pressure across the NHS. This would allow it to bring in the 'best and brightest' from the financial sector to provide expert advice on repayment and renegotiation (some on a pro bono basis). Furthermore, it could offer a timely indicator to all, including the European Commission, that the NHS holds a status of national protection unique among UK services, preserving its founding ethos. Finally, the whole innovation would be designed to fall outside the calculation of the government's public expenditure borrowing requirement and utilise new streams of taxation.

For example, I would argue that there is a strong case, now that the National Lottery option is closed to the NHS, for funding the NHS Investment Fund from gambling taxes, phased in through a government grant periodically as needed. From 1 December 2014, changes will come into effect so that certain gambling taxes (general betting duty, pool betting duty, and remote gaming duty) will be charged on a 'place of consumption' basis, rather than a 'place of supply' basis. The supply of remote gambling to UK customers from outside the UK will become liable to a UK gambling tax for the first time.[128] Initial setting-up costs of the fund and new investments would be covered by passing to the fund the money collected from the new online gambling tax, due to be levied from 10 December 2014. In the financial year 2015/16 earmarking money to the Trust by government decision could probably take place without legislation, given that the government has supported the Olympics and other such big projects of national importance which set them apart from general capital and revenue support. Otherwise it could be dealt with in the Finance Bill presented annually. It might, of course, if there was a consensus, become part of the NHS Reinstatement Bill 2015. The fifteen per cent online gambling tax is expected to raise as much as £300 million a year. The five per cent additional tax increase due to be collected from bookmakers from the end of March 2015 is expected to raise £75 million. This sum of around £375 million, though not yet formally allocated elsewhere, would already be taken into account by the Treasury for the first year of the fund's operation. For this it would be supplemented with other money from the existing collection of gambling taxes.

A further funding method that could be popular and tie in with the growing political and public concern is to target the revenue lost through non-payment and avoidance of tax,

---

128 'Remote Gambling Bill receives royal assent', Gov.uk, 15 May 2014.

which exceeds £34 billion per year.[129] Significant public anger has been directed towards companies perceived as able to avoid paying their 'fair share' through avoidance schemes or by exploiting legislation. Indeed, the PCS union sees these HMRC figures as a gross underestimate, putting the true tax gap at over £100 billion. It is high time that public and political anger on this matter was exercised. In doing so, a large revenue stream would be opened up that would provide crucial support in PFI payment. The ins and outs of what is included in or excluded from the PSBR is rather like what Kremlinology contributed to the old Soviet Union. Whether the charitable route would be productive can be examined in the Treasury, but since one of the reasons for not consolidating through the Treasury is the PSBR implications, these matters will have to be explored. But a charitable route has many unquestionable benefits.

The NHS Investment Fund will not be a device to open the contracts and reveal the high costs of PFI, at least initially, but negotiations would start over full transparency. At the moment the Treasury has parked departmental PFIs, almost admitting they are just too difficult to change. But a charitable fund would have room for horse-trading over the central PFI schemes in return for other contracts that they would hold and any future PFI contracts they might undertake. There is certainly merit in centralising all the contracts and the funding and negotiating of the contracts and buybacks. It would also end NHS hospital foundation trusts having to deal with resource accounting and capital charging, and the local affordability problems and distortions, as well as making it easier to rationalise foundation

---

129 *The Guardian*, 11 October 2013.

trust status and paving the way for their becoming part of any new health authorities that might emerge under the enabling provisions of the NHS Reinstatement Bill 2015.

Recent statistics on the health component of the government's use of PFIs are contained within the Treasury report *Private Finance Initiative Projects: 2013 Summary Data* (December 2013). In December 2012, the Treasury published a document outlining the government's new approach to managing PFIs,[130] having reassessed how they are used. The House of Commons Treasury Committee considered this revised approach. There was a discussion of the 'comparison of procurement options' on pages 23–4, which states that 'under PFI, all projects had to complete a Value for Money (VFM) assessment of the PFI option compared to a conventional procurement option funded directly by central government. This was known as the PSC (Public Sector Comparator).'

Whether a PFI is deemed 'value for money' can be found in another Treasury document, *Value for Money Assessment Guidance*. When publishing its revised guidelines on the use of PFIs in December 2012, the Treasury stated that 'the Government will develop and consult on guidance which will replace the existing Value for Money Assessment Guide'.[131] However, no further information has since been published on this.

In a Civitas report, *PFI: Still the Only Game in Town*, the author, Elliot Bidgood, outlined a number of possible alternatives to using PFIs. This included the possibility of using a 'non-profit

---

130 HM Treasury, *A New Approach to Public Private Partnerships*, December 2012.
131 Ibid., p. 13.

distribution' (NPD) model, which is set out on page 11: 'NPD is similar to PFI in basic design, but has contractors invest solely in project debt and it is 100% debt-funded, with no expensive private equity element. It also caps returns to investors, diverting surpluses into a non-governmental charity for the public (hence the reference to it being non-profit distributing.'

The NHS Reinstatement Bill 2015 may examine other ways of handling PFIs. We need to remove the problems of PFI debt and affordability for NHS managers. Given that there is no support for it to be added to the PSBR, and that PFI debts are consolidated in Scotland, finding a solution to the lack of value for money and the risk costs of PFI is an important issue. Successive governments have tried to tackle public expenditure rules, many of which are designed or executed to prevent public ownership. While gambling levies are thought to be a regressive means of taxation by some, this may change slowly with the taxing of online gambling. There may be different ways to finance the NHS other than by creating a charitable trust to buy back contracts and change public expenditure rules. But any scheme has real attractions for the NHS. Creating an NHS charitable investment fund has an added advantage of showing that the NHS is *sui generis*. It could attract industry experts who having made a lot of money might be willing to contribute their knowledge. A Fund of the type suggested could be a popular way of introducing new money into the NHS with the potential of providing immediate relief for trust and foundation trust hospitals facing growing deficits.

Why am I convinced that in 2015 a campaign for an NHS Reinstatement Bill can succeed? The answer lies in part in the fact that something not dissimilar but on a much more modest scale was proved to work in 2010. Given the distinct possibility that that year's general election would result in a hung parliament, decision makers were about to face an electoral result that few had predicted and even fewer had much knowledge of how to handle. What was needed was that the Labour government, the Conservative opposition and the Liberal Democrats in particular would know how to proceed if, despite their own parties' hopes of winning power outright, that expectation turned out to be wrong. A website, Charter 2010, was formally launched in January that year as an independent initiative supported by an a small all-party group of politicians, businessmen and women, academics and opinion formers who advocated that the parties should plan *before the election* of 2010 in case of a hung parliament.

In fact the website had been planned since October 2009 – when the bookmakers were offering 5-1 against a hung parliament. At the same time I wrote in *The Times* an edited extract from my revised and shortened autobiography[132] which considered the possibility, despite their commanding lead in the polls, that the Conservatives would not gain an overall majority at the upcoming election. Neither I nor Mike Thomas, a former SDP MP and co-founders of Charter 2010, were members of a political party. As Labour MPs we had lived through the Labour government of 1974–9 with a small or non-existent majority. It had struggled with an inherited oil and financial crisis from the tail end of Edward Heath's government of 1970–74 and had delayed adopting tough economic measures on coming into office with no working majority, first in order to get a larger

---

132 David Owen, *Time to Declare: Second Innings* (Politico's, 2009).

majority via a second general election, held in October 1974, then because of the need to win the referendum to stay in the European Community, as it was then called, in June 1975. The retirement of Harold Wilson as Prime Minister in 1976 meant that his successor, Jim Callaghan, had to preside over the days of economic reckoning, which came that autumn. Callaghan decided courageously that we could not spend our way out of the crisis. The government under IMF constraints survived predominantly because of deals with Northern Ireland MPs, and the Lib–Lab Pact of 1976–78, negotiated with David Steel, sometimes helped, until it lost a vote of no confidence in spring 1979.

The Charter 2010 website provided information on – and neutral ground for discussion of – the implications of a hung parliament and a lot of relevant polling information when all the parties were only talking about and planning for winning outright. Its statement of objectives was designed for members of all political parties and in summarised form read: 'There is no immutable law within the UK constitutional system that says that, however narrow its electoral support, the political party winning the largest number of seats in a general election is obliged to seek to govern on its own.' It called on the leaders of the parties to be 'open-minded about forming in 2010 a government made up of more than one party as the best way of handling the crisis facing the country.' It continued that there were immense political and economic dangers ahead if we failed to plan now for the possibility of a continuing economic crisis and that the international financial community would need the assurance of a coherent, credible and lasting government to emerge out of a hung parliament.

The background to the charter has some relevance to the Campaign for the NHS Reinstatement Bill 2015. Both are about changing people's minds before and during a general election campaign. Annex E contains first a longer description of Charter 2010 and also extracts from its website for readers who wish to understand its operation in more detail.

There was little comfort for Labour or the Conservatives in the poll. The Labour government under Tony Blair had been re-elected for a third time in 2005 but with only 35 per cent of the total vote. Most polls put the Conservatives in 2009 around 40 per cent. However, when asked 'What would be the best outcome for Britain in terms of dealing sensibly with the country's major problems?', only 30 per cent of those polled thought 'A government made up of a single political party'. Seven in ten preferred 'A government made up of a coalition of parties'. Blair had in seats won a comfortable majority in 2005 but it was far from whole hearted. It is a salutary thought that by 2015 Britain will have had ten years' rule by governments for which there has been no great popular enthusiasm.

For the Liberal Democrats there was an interesting and relevant finding. About the same number of voters would support them if they believed they would hold the balance of power in the House of Commons (31 per cent) as would if they thought the Lib Dems would get a majority (29 per cent). This meant, if they had the courage to follow its findings, that there was no need for the Liberal Democrats to campaign only on what many saw as an unrealistic platform of 'winning' the election. They would command just as much support if they talked openly about plans to cooperate with other parties in the event of a hung parliament. And significantly more than they would receive if people believed they would 'only win a few seats' (17 per cent). Such have been the travails of the coalition from 2010 that these polling findings may not apply in 2015.

It became obvious within days of our website launch on 14 January 2010 that a hung parliament was more than likely to emerge. The public wanted the parties to work together to solve Britain's problems. They saw, well before the political leaders, the sense of a stable multi-party supported government, which would have majority electoral support. They wanted the parties to put aside narrow interests for the national interest. Some, of course, continued up to May 2010 to believe that an unstable minority government was desirable and felt that with the usual political manoeuvring the threat of a second election could be held off for a year or more, rather like Harold Wilson had done after the 1964 general election until he called another election in 1966 and won by a large majority.

I had had a working breakfast with Nick Clegg hosted by Lord Alliance, a Liberal Democrat peer and a longstanding friend of mine, on 16 November 2009. On the Labour side, contact was established with a number of senior figures in Gordon Brown's government, and through Danny Finkelstein, a friend from SDP days, we were confident that information was going to George Osborne and that the message was reaching David Cameron.

By 5 May 2010, the site had had over 52,000 hits and more than 1,300 people on average were logging on each day. That was pretty good given we had chosen a target audience which was relatively small: the 1,000 potential MPs and candidates with a real chance of winning their seat, 100 influential members of the House of Lords, 50 journalists, 20 academics and civil servants and 100 key party figures or 'apparatchiks'. As the general election approached we felt we were probably reaching a much higher proportion of these key figures or their staff on a regular basis. The website provided a comprehensive summary of the constitutional and economic issues relating to a hung parliament and of day-by-day press coverage. The polling evidence became so compelling that more and more columnists started to cover the issue. All of this and much more can be achieved in 2015 with an effective campaign to persuade candidates to reinstate the NHS in England if they are elected as an MP. The fundamental campaigning tool will be our website, www.nhsbill2015.org.

At Charter 2010 we never took the cynics' view that it was too much to hope that David Cameron, Gordon Brown, Nick Clegg and their colleagues would take a realistic approach in the event of a hung parliament. Indeed, the political price of *not* responding to the public mood after the indecisive election in 2010 soon became very clear. All three in their various ways responded. But the one who had the most difficulty in responding was Gordon Brown, in part because he was the one in power and the election was his to lose. The same change of mind can be achieved in 2015 about the essential need to replace the 2012 NHS legislation immediately after the election.

In the event David Cameron's 'big, bold and comprehensive offer' to work with the Liberal Democrats in government was more of a shock to MPs and the existing British political structures than to the general public. The party political 'taboo' on candidates as well as the lead players and their media supporters openly discussing a hung parliament during the election campaign had been based on the conventional wisdom that any such discussion would be seized upon as a sign of weakness or even impending defeat. At an early stage it became clear that some Labour MPs seemed happier to opt for becoming the official opposition. They had been in majority governments for thirteen years; they were in a number of cases against the very thought of sharing power with the Liberal Democrats, who had been critical of Labour from a position on the left but now seemed ready to join the Conservatives in a rightist government. Conservative MPs, out of office for those thirteen years, were hungry for power. But in truth 2010 was an amazing result and it was a sign of political weakness that Cameron could not win outright against Brown.

In January 2010 the wall of silence from the politicians on the issue of an impending hung parliament was hard to surmount. We developed a number of techniques. First was the Hung Parliament Index: this translated poll results into seats in parliament using a widely accepted formula. The results were plotted on a table the centre of which was highlighted as the Hung Parliament Zone (HPZ). To our surprise, well before the end of January 2010, the line started to dip into the HPZ, and it pretty well stayed there until 6 May.

We were not, of course, alone in our extra-parliamentary endeavour to draw the attention of the political establishment to the need to plan for a hung parliament. The then Cabinet Secretary and head of the civil service, Sir Gus O'Donnell, took a very important and influential role particularly when giving evidence to the House of Commons Justice Select Committee, chaired by Sir Alan Beith. In the academic world, the Constitution Unit at University College London made significant contributions to the discussion and, among others, that journalist/academic hybrid Peter Riddell of *The Times* was writing knowledgeably and influentially on the subject throughout the period. O'Donnell also played a crucial role in the negotiations that led to the formation of the coalition government. Perhaps, if, as has been said, he was the midwife to the birth of the coalition, Charter 2010 can properly claim to have provided some ante-natal classes!

Charter 2010 published early in January a nationwide survey of the voters' reactions to a hung parliament. The results were revealing: nearly nine in ten voters (89 per cent) believed that, in the event of a hung parliament, it would be 'in Britain's best interests for the political parties to work together and try to agree on measures to address the country's economic and financial crisis'. Three quarters wanted the parties to agree that there should not be another election for four years and for the parties to work together to solve the country's problems. Only a quarter believed that a hung result should be followed by 'a second general election to try to get a majority for one party'.

Charter 2010 tried to seek the views on a hung parliament of all parliamentary candidates – primarily as a way of getting our message over to them – and published on the website replies of those who responded. But we never managed to make big inroads into changing the mindsets of candidates, mainly because we did not have the activists on the ground in any numbers that were necessary to prompt replies and persuade candidates. But the seed of an idea for the future was sown, which will be of considerable relevance for 2015. The Campaign for the NHS Reinstatement Bill has the potential to mobilise sufficient activists concerned about the NHS to prompt replies and vigorously pursue those candidates who do not wish to reply.

What we did pick up in 2010 is that a much larger proportion of Liberal Democrat candidates than of any other party replied, but this was probably due to the traditional Liberal Party interest in constitutional matters and their wish to hold the balance in negotiations over proportional representation. In 2015 Liberal Democrat interest in health matters does not as yet appear likely to be as strong but the Campaign for the NHS Reinstatement Bill 2015 will seek to change that and persuade candidates and MPs to be more critical of their support from the fundamentally flawed NHS legislation of 2012. But we do not intend to ignore Conservative candidates and MPs and the EU implications for the NHS are becoming ever more apparent to UKIP candidates and MPs.

It cannot be ignored that the senior NHS national leadership, in its broadest sense as distinct from rank-and-file nurses, managers and doctors, has supported at every stage legislation that is now admitted by coalition politicians to have been a massive blunder. 'THE NHS REFORMS OUR WORST MISTAKE, TORIES ADMIT' was the banner headline on the front page of *The Times* on 13 October 2014. Mistakes have to be corrected – that is the core message of the Campaign for the NHS Reinstatement Bill 2015 and the more it is done as a result of people pressure the better. The politicians cannot be ignored but at a general election, if democracy means anything, they must listen and learn from their mistakes.

The so-called 'aligned national NHS Leadership' are all appointees. They tell us they have 'distinctive national duties laid on them by statute'. NHS England and Monitor in the report tell the next government and Parliament of 'a mismatch between resources and patient needs of nearly £30 billion a year by

2020/21' and that it can be closed 'by one third (£21 billion), one half (£16 billion) or all the way'. The NHS Leadership then brief the press – for it is not included in their report – that they will settle for a government subvention of their spending of £8 billion and will make efficiency savings of £22 billion, but, incidentally, not telling anyone how they will be achieved. This is a very big ask, to use the jargon of today's public relations industry.

Let us all pause before we get carried away by this PR document. I am firmly in favour of more public spending on the NHS and ready to pay a 49.9 per cent higher tax rate or exceptionally more to help finance it, but we need as citizens to avoid being carried away by NHS England's special pleading, which we incidentally have paid for, and make it the basis for our public spending demands. What if the same thing were to be undertaken by the 'National Leadership' of Education, Housing, the Police, the Crown Courts? What if the armed services of the Crown were now to be allowed to produce a similar document signed off by its 'National Leadership', the Chief of the Defence Staff, the Chief of the Naval Staff, the Chief of the Army and the Chief of the Air Staff, accompanied by their single service logos with no reference to the Secretary of State for Defence? Are Cameron and Osborne going to allow all public spending bodies to be able to conduct themselves in this way? Would such a display be encouraged as an example of independence and wisdom? Or would it be an example of vested-interest log rolling and irresponsibility? Only when those questions are posed is it possible to identify the underlying flaws in the autonomy clause of the Health and Social Care Act 2012 that allow NHS England to behave in this way. That Act has unleashed a completely new form of democratic governance with huge national health quangos assembled and granted powers of autonomy to make demands and push for an independence that would be challenging even in good economic circumstances, let alone in those that will face this country after the general election in 2015.

There used to be a famous BBC radio programme with Wilfred Pickles whose gag lines were 'What's on the table, Mabel?' and 'Give 'em the money, Barney'. Never before has there been introduced such an unworkable mechanism for settling the spending priorities of a democratic government. The Treasury and the Chancellor of the Exchequer, having lost control of the costings of the NHS, will have to re-establish a measure of control. Ministers in other departments will begin to realise what has been unleashed. Parliament, likewise, will not be ready to see such a pre-emption of resources without scrutiny and debate. It does no service to the NHS for the *Five Year Forward View* to add to their pretensions by claiming that the present legislative framework and the autonomy clause are viable. To be told by the National Leadership of the NHS that 'there is now quite a broad consensus on what a better future should be' makes one ask: what is their definition of 'quite'? It is certainly not a 'quiet' broad consensus, to judge by the mounting clamour of criticism throughout the NHS about its marketisation and commercialisation. Yet the National Leadership appears to believe this can all be ignored. It knows without acknowledging the public debate that its model is the correct one for the NHS. But the evidence, such as it exists, is to the contrary.

This book shows in some detail how flawed have been the decisions already made by many of those involved in this National Leadership, over Lewisham Hospital and Tower

Hamlets GPs to name but two. The Alliance for Healthcare Competitiveness (AHC), in which the new chief executive of NHS England, Simon Stevens, was so involved when in the US, is still pushing for the inclusion of the investor–state dispute settlement, ISDS, in the TTIP and against any exemption for bodies such as the NHS. Were this to succeed there will be many more American companies doing business in the UK and focused even more on our NHS. Fortunately, all the signs are that the new European Commission will be prevented from signing up to these provisions and there will be more negotiations. After 2015, we in the UK must press for a very different outcome for the TTIP, one which protects our NHS and the health services of other EU member states. We are not alone on this issue in the UK. The campaign intends to find out where existing MPs and parliamentary candidates stand on these issues as well as all the others relating to the NHS.

The NHS needs, from whatever political party or parties that form the next government, an acceptance that all cannot be business as usual in the UK health services. The people will hopefully have exerted their right to insist on reinstating a democratic NHS in England, one where there is an accountable leadership – from Parliament to Cabinet to the Secretary of State for Health. There will, I am sure, be more money found for the NHS in the UK generally, not as much as I would want, nor as much as the NHS needs. But a reinstated NHS will be far better placed to provide a cost-effective comprehensive healthcare service, similar but not the same in all parts of the UK. This is what the NHS has done for sixty-eight years, providing a health service which our Parliament has decided we can afford as a country rather than the expensive US-based model. Dismantling that NHS and continuing with the Health and Social Care Act 2012 the electorate will not accept.

This 2012 *external* market, if it is allowed to stand unamended in its present legislative form after the general election in 2015, will have a deep and damaging impact on the behaviour of health professionals in the NHS and on depressing standards of care. It will challenge the very nature of the vocational aspect of medicine for nurses and doctors and indeed everyone who works in the NHS. It may happen slowly but the dynamics of the market over the years will carry their own momentum. It will also alter the relationship of trust between patients and doctors and patients and nurses as well as other healthcare professionals. The NHS in this market system will not be rationed by democratic choice but eventually by the patient's capacity to pay through insurance premiums and charges. We will not be able to rely on what is basically a fair and open system but will have to take our chances on the vagaries of a marketplace. That system will not be an NHS in any true meaning of the term, however many NHS logos are stuck on private enterprises. Patients will be left fearing, sometimes correctly, that what is presented as a general practitioner's decision is so in name only. In reality the decision will have been made not predominantly on clinical grounds but on the basis of cost. When that perception becomes understood as reality it will irrevocably harm the patient–physician or patient–nurse relationship. The same does not apply in the purely private sector, where the patient pays either through insurance or in cash considerable sums of money in the expectation of one-to-one advice which will not be influenced by affordability. This is the essential difference to grasp between private and public medicine. Public medicine is controlled by democratic decision making. The old cry 'Keep politics out of the NHS' was unachievable and many of its supporters, confronted by the market model, are, I suspect, like others, having second thoughts. Public provision has to have the accountability that comes with democracy. There cannot be a total free licence for those who manage an essential public service like the NHS. To pretend that there can is one of the most disingenuous parts of the 2012 legislation and this is but one of many, many reasons why the NHS Reinstatement Bill 2015 will be such a key element for decision by voters in this forthcoming general election.

The end of the NHS as we have known and understood it in England will take place before 2020 if whichever party or parties that win the 2015 general election does not change the 2012 NHS legislation. Social historians may not be agreed as to when the exact moment of its passing will be. As endings go, it will be, in the words of T. S. Eliot, 'not with a bang but a whimper'. Very likely around that moment the issue of Scottish independence will be back on the political agenda. The two are linked in more ways than have yet been fully recognised.

In his first inaugural address Abraham Lincoln finished with these words: 'The mystic clouds of memory, stretching from every battlefield and patriot grave to every living heart and hearthstone all over this broad land, will yet swell the chorus of the Union when again touched, as surely they will be, by the better angels of our nature.' The NHS is not a 'religion', as it has been likened to, nor is it the preserve of one political party, nor one country within our United Kingdom. It belongs to all of us and it quite simply represents the better angels of our nature.

Annex A

National Health Service (Amended Duties and Powers) Bill [HL]

A BILL TO Re-establish the Secretary of State's legal duty as to the National Health Service in England, Quangos and related bodies.

BE IT ENACTED by the Queen's most Excellent Majesty, by and with the advice and consent of the Lords Spiritual and Temporal, and Commons, in this present Parliament assembled, and by the authority of the same, as follows:

1. Secretary of State's duties to promote and provide a comprehensive and integrated health service

For section 1 of the National Health Service Act 2006 (Secretary of State's duty to promote comprehensive health service) substitute—

'1. Secretary of State's duty as to the health service

    1) It shall be the duty of the Secretary of State to promote in England a comprehensive and integrated health service designed to secure improvement—

a) in the physical and mental health of the people of England, and

b) in the prevention, diagnosis and treatment of illness, and for that purpose to provide or secure the effective provision of services in accordance with this Act.

2) The services so provided must be free of charge except in so far as the making and recovery of charges is expressly provided for, by or under any enactment, whenever passed.

3) The services provided pursuant to this Act and to the Health and Social Care Act 2012, howsoever or by whom so ever provided, secured or arranged, shall be deemed to be provided in furtherance of the duty to provide or secure effective provision of services under subsection (1).'

2.   Abolition of the duties of autonomy

1) Sections 1D and 13F of the National Health Service Act 2006 (duties as to promoting autonomy) are repealed.

3.   Concurrent duty of and commissioning by the NHS Commissioning Board

1) Section 1H(2) of the National Health Service Act 2006 is repealed.

1) In section 1H(3) of that Act, for 'For the purpose of discharging that duty', substitute 'For the purpose of furthering the duty of the Secretary of State under section 1(1)'.

4. Secretary of State's duty as to provision of certain services

1) Section 3 of the National Health Service Act 2006 is amended as follows.

2) Before subsection (1) insert—

'(A1) The Secretary of State must provide, or secure the effective provision of, throughout England, to such extent as he considers necessary to meet all reasonable requirements, the accommodation, services and facilities set out in subsection (1) (a) to (f).'

3) In subsection (1), before 'A' insert 'For that purpose,'.

5. Powers of directions to Quangos and other bodies

1) The Secretary of State may direct any of the bodies mentioned in subsection (2) to exercise any functions relating to the health service which are specified in the directions, and may also give directions to any such body about its exercise of any functions or about its provision of services under arrangements referred to in subsection (2)(h).

2) These bodies are—

a) the National Health Service Commissioning Board,

b) a clinical commissioning group,

c) a Special Health Authority,

d) an NHS trust,

e) an NHS foundation trust,

f) the National Institute for Health and Care Excellence,

g) the Health and Social Care Information Centre, and

h) any other body or person providing services in pursuance of arrangements made—

   i) by the Secretary of State under section 12 of,

   ii) by the Board or a clinical commissioning group under section 3, 3A, 3B, 4 of or Schedule 1 to,

   iii) by a local authority for the purpose of the exercise of its functions under or by virtue of section 2B or 6C(1) of or Schedule 1 to, or

iv) by the Board, a clinical commissioning group or a local authority by virtue of section 7A of, the National Health Service Act 2006.

3) In exercising his power under subsection (1), the Secretary of State must have regard to the desirability, so far as consistent with the interests of the health service and relevant to the exercise of the power in all circumstances—

a) of protecting and promoting the health of patients and the public;

b) of any bodies mentioned in subsection (2) being free, in exercising its functions or providing services in accordance with its duties and powers, to do so in the manner that it considers best calculated to promote the comprehensive and integrated service referred to in section 1(1) of the National Health Service Act 2006; and

c) of ensuring co-operation between the bodies mentioned in subsection (2) in the exercise of their functions or provision of services.

4) If, in having regard to the desirability of the matters referred to in subsection (3) the Secretary of State considers that there is a conflict between those matters and the discharge of his duties under section 1 of the National Health Service Act 2006, he must give priority to the duties under that section.

6. Monitor

1) The Health and Social Care Act 2012 is amended as follows.

2) After section 61 insert—

'61A Monitor's objective

1) The objective of Monitor is to contribute to the achievement

of a comprehensive and integrated health service in England through the exercise of its functions.

2) In exercising its main duty and other functions Monitor must act in accordance with that objective and in a manner consistent with the performance by the Secretary of State of his duties contained in sections 1 and 3 of the National Health Service Act 2006.'

3) Section 62(9) is repealed.

7. Amendment to competition requirements

1) Section 75 of the Health and Social Care Act 2012 (requirements as to procurement, patient choice and competition) is amended as follows.

2) For paragraph (c) of subsection (1) substitute—

'(c) are free so to commission such services which best serve patients' interests and with no impediments to beneficial co-operation to increase integration, improve quality or reduce inequalities;'.

3) After paragraph (c) of subsection (1), insert—

'(d) will have a full range of options and will be under no legal obligation to foster markets, particularly where competition would not be effective in driving high standards and value for patients.'

3) The National Health Service (Procurement, Patient Choice and Competition) (No. 2) Regulations 2013 are repealed.

8. Public register of NHS contracts

1) Each NHS body shall establish and maintain a public register of contracts entered into by it in relation to the provision of health services.

2) The register shall be available electronically and for inspection by the public at all reasonable hours and copies of the documents on the register shall be provided on request at reasonable cost.

3) The Secretary of State shall make regulations to make further provision regarding the public register.

4) In subsection (1) 'contracts' includes documents presented in relation to the contracts, and sub-contracts.

9. Treaty requirements

1) No treaty which requires the United Kingdom—

   (a) to change; or

   (b) to limit the powers of the United Kingdom in respect of,

   NHS legislation shall be signed or agreed unless any such changes or limits have been approved by—

   i) in relation to England, an Act of Parliament;

   ii) in relation to Scotland, an Act of the Scottish Parliament;

   iii) in relation to Wales, an Act of the National Assembly for Wales; and

   iv) in relation to Northern Ireland, an Act of the Northern Ireland Assembly.

2) In subsection (1)—

   'to change' means to amend, repeal, introduce or otherwise to change; 'NHS legislation' means any primary legislation passed by Parliament, the Scottish Parliament, the National Assembly for Wales or the Northern Ireland Assembly, and any secondary legislation enacted by the Secretary of State or any of the devolved administrations, relating to—

   (a) as regards England, the comprehensive health service which must be continued under section 1(1) of the National Health Service Act 2006;

(b) as regards Scotland, the comprehensive and integrated health service that must be continued under section 1(1) of the National Health Service (Scotland) Act 1978;

(c) as regards Wales, the comprehensive health service that must be continued under section 1(1) of the National Health Service (Wales) Act 2006; and

(d) as regards Northern Ireland, the integrated health services and personal social services that must be provided or secured under Article 4 of the Health and Personal Social Services (Northern Ireland) Order 1972;

'treaty' means a written agreement between States or between States and international organisations which is binding under international law and includes any protocol, annex or schedule to or an amendment or replacement of such an agreement and includes a regulation, rule, measure, decision or similar instrument made under a treaty, which has the effect mentioned in subsection (1).

10. Interpretation

Expressions used in this Act which are also in the National Health Service Act 2006 and in the Health and Social Care Act 2012 shall have the same meanings as the meanings given to those expressions under those Acts.

11. Short title, commencement and extent

1) This Act may be cited as the National Health Service (Amended Duties and Powers) Act 2013.

2) This Act shall come into force on the day on which it is passed.

3) This Act extends to England, except section 9 which extends to England and Wales, Northern Ireland and Scotland.

Annex B

National Health Service (Amended Duties and Powers) Bill

A BILL TO re-establish the Secretary of State's legal duty to provide national health services in England, to amend the provisions of the Health and Social Care Act 2012 relating to Monitor; to repeal the Regulations made under section 75 of that Act; to make other amendments to the provisions in that Act relating to competition and provision of private health services; and for connected purposes.

BE IT ENACTED by the Queen's most Excellent Majesty, by and with the advice and consent of the Lords Spiritual and Temporal, and Commons, in this present Parliament assembled, and by the authority of the same, as follows:—

PART 1

AMENDMENTS TO SECTIONS WITHIN PART 1 OF THE
NATIONAL HEALTH SERVICE ACT 2006, AS AMENDED BY
THE HEALTH AND SOCIAL CARE ACT 2012

1. Duty on the Secretary of State to promote comprehensive health service based on social solidarity

For section 1 of the National Health Service Act 2006 as amended by section 1 of the Health and Social Care Act 2012 (Secretary of State's duty to promote health service) substitute—

'**1. Secretary of State's duty to promote comprehensive health service based on social solidarity**

1) The Secretary of State must continue the promotion in England of a comprehensive health service designed to secure improvement—

(a) in the physical and mental health of the people of England, and

(b) in the prevention, diagnosis and treatment of physical and mental illness.

2) For that purpose, the Secretary of State must:

(a) exercise the functions conferred by this Act so as to secure that services are provided in accordance with this Act;

(b) ensure that the health service is a public service which delivers services of general economic interest and operates on the basis of social solidarity; and

(c) ensure that arrangements between commissioners and providers of health services require effective co-operation between different providers under this Act and between providers of health services and providers of community care services.

3) The Secretary of State retains ministerial responsibility to Parliament for the provision of the health service in England.

4) The services provided as part of the health service in England must be free of charge except in so far as the making and recovery of charges is expressly provided for by or under any enactment, whenever passed.'

2. Exercise of the Secretary of State's powers

After section 2B of the National Health Service Act 2006 insert—

'2C. Duties and guidance in respect of cooperation and social solidarity

1) The Secretary of State shall exercise his powers under this Act to promote the health service as an efficient service based on mutual cooperation and social solidarity and so as to ensure that that any person who is concerned in commissioning or providing health services for the purposes of the health service—

   (a) adheres to such practices in relation to procurement as the Secretary of State identifies as being appropriate for the purposes of the health service;

   (b) protects and promotes the right of patients to make choices with respect to treatment or other health care services provided for the purposes of the health service, in as much as the exercise of such choice is consistent with the overall interests of the health service;

   (v) does not engage in anti-competitive or any other behaviour which the Secretary of State considers is against the interests of people who use health services.

2) The Secretary of State shall be entitled to publish guidance for health service commissioners and providers concerning the matters set out in sub-section (1) above and where

such guidance is published all health service commissioners and providers shall give due regard to the guidance when discharging any relevant function.

3) The Secretary of State shall be entitled to seek such advice concerning the matter set out in sub-section (1) from such persons as he considers fit.

4) The Secretary of State may issue directions to any health service body to support the discharge of the functions under sub-section (1).

5) If any dispute arises with respect to whether any health service body or other person providing health service services has acted in accordance with the matters set out in sub-section (1) or has otherwise acted in a way that is anti-competitive or contrary to the interests of the health service, any health service body or provider of services under the National Health Service Act 2006 may refer a complaint to the Secretary of State.

6) Where a complaint is made under sub-section (5) above the Secretary of State shall be entitled to adjudicate upon the complaint or to appoint a person to adjudicate upon the complaint if the Secretary of State considers that it is appropriate to do so.

7) Any adjudication under this section shall be final and binding for all purposes.'

3. Duty on the Secretary of State regarding provision of certain services

1) For section 3 of the National Health Service Act 2006 (Secretary of State's duty to promote health service) as amended by section 13 of the Health and Social Care Act 2012 substitute—

'3. Secretary of State's duty as to provision of certain services

1) The Secretary of State must arrange for the provision of the following to such extent as he considers necessary to meet all reasonable requirements—

   (a) hospital accommodation,

   (b) other accommodation for the purpose of any service provided under this Act,

   (c) medical, dental, ophthalmic, nursing and ambulance services,

   (d) such other services or facilities for the care of pregnant women, women who are breastfeeding and young children as he considers are appropriate as part of the health service,

   (e) such other services or facilities for the prevention of illness, the care of persons suffering from illness and the after-care of persons who have suffered from illness as he considers are appropriate as part of the health service,

   (f) such other services or facilities as are required for the diagnosis and treatment of illness.

1) The Secretary of State shall be entitled to delegate all or any part of the performance of the duty under sub-section (1) above to the Board.

2) The Secretary of State may give directions to the Board concerning the performance of the duty under sub-section (1).

3) The Secretary of State shall be entitled to delegate the performance of the duty under sub-section (1) above to a clinical commissioning group for—

   (a) persons who are provided with primary medical services by a member of the group,

    (b) persons who usually reside in the group's area and are not provided with primary medical services by a member of any clinical commissioning group, and

    (c) any other category of persons as set out in a Direction made by the Secretary of State.

5) The Secretary of State may give directions to a clinical commissioning group concerning the performance of the duty under sub-section (1).'

4. Provision of high security psychiatric services

For section 4 of the National Health Service Act 2006 as amended by section 16 of the Health and Social Care Act 2012 substitute—

'4. Provision of high security psychiatric services

1) The Secretary of State must arrange for the provision of hospital accommodation and services for persons who—

    (a) are liable to be detained under the Mental Health Act 1983, and

    (b) in the opinion of the Secretary of State require treatment under conditions of high security on account of their dangerous, violent or criminal propensities.

1) The Secretary of State may delegate all or any part of the performance of the duty under sub-section (1) above to the Board.

2) The Secretary of State may give directions to the Board concerning the performance of the duty under sub-section (1).

3) The hospital accommodation and services mentioned in subsection (1) are referred to in this section and paragraph 15 of Schedule 4 (NHS trusts) as "high security psychiatric services".'

5. Power of Secretary of State to direct certain health service bodies

For section 8 of the National Health Service Act 2006 substitute—

'8. Secretary of State's directions to certain health service bodies

1) The Secretary of State may give directions to any of the bodies mentioned in subsection (2) about its exercise of any functions

2) The bodies are—

    (a) clinical commissioning groups,

    (b) the Board,

    (c) NHS Trusts, and

    (d) Special Health Authorities.

3) Nothing in provision made by or under this or any other Act affects the generality of subsection (1).'

6. NHS Contracts

For section 9 of the National Health Service Act 2006 substitute—

'9. NHS Contracts

1) In this Act, an NHS contract is an arrangement under which one health service body ("the commissioner") arranges for the provision to it by another health service body ("the provider") of goods or services which it reasonably requires for the purposes of its functions.

2) Section 139(6) (NHS contracts and the provision of local pharmaceutical services under pilot schemes) makes further provision about acting as commissioner for the purposes of subsection (1).

3) Paragraph 15 of Schedule 4 (NHS trusts and NHS contracts) makes further provision about an NHS trust acting as provider for the purposes of subsection (1).

4) "Health service body" means any of the following—

(a) the Board,

(b) a clinical commissioning group,

(c) an NHS trust,

(d) an NHS Foundation Trust,

(e) a Special Health Authority,

(f) a Local Health Board,

(g) a Health Board constituted under section 2 of the National Health Service (Scotland) Act 1978,

(h) a Special Health Board constituted under that section,

(i) a Health and Social Services Board constituted under the Health and Personal Social Services (Northern Ireland) Order 1972 (SI 1972/1265 (NI14)),

(j) the Common Services Agency for the Scottish Health Service,

(k) the Wales Centre for Health,

(l) the Care Quality Commission,

(m) National Institute for Health and Care Excellence,

(n) the Health and Social Care Information Centre,

(o) the Scottish Dental Practice Board,

(p) the Secretary of State,

(q) the Welsh Ministers,

(r) the Scottish Ministers,

(s) Healthcare Improvement Scotland,

(t) the Northern Ireland Central Services Agency for the Health and Social Services established under the Health and Personal Social Services (Northern Ireland) Order 1972,

(u) a special health and social services agency established under the Health and Personal Social Services (Special

Agencies) (Northern Ireland) Order 1990 (SI 1990/247 (NI3)),

(v) a Health and Social Services trust established under the Health and Personal Social Services (Northern Ireland) Order 1991 (SI 1991/194 (NI1)),

(w) the Department of Health, Social Services and Public Safety,

(x) a local authority exercising functions under this Act.

5) An arrangement for the provision of goods or services by a health service body with a person who is not a health service body shall also take effect as an NHS contract if—

(a) the terms of the arrangement are reduced to writing or evidenced in writing; and

(b) the parties to the arrangement have recorded in writing that the arrangement shall operate as an NHS contract.

6) Whether or not an arrangement which constitutes an NHS contract would apart from this subsection be a contract in law, it must not be regarded for any purpose as giving rise to contractual rights or liabilities.

7) If any dispute arises with respect to such an arrangement, either party may refer the matter to the Secretary of State for determination under this section.

8) If, in the course of negotiations intending to lead to an arrangement which will be an NHS contract, it appears to a health service body—

(a) that the terms proposed by another health service body are unfair by reason that the other is seeking to take advantage of its position as the only, or the only practicable, provider of the goods or services concerned or by reason of any other unequal bargaining position as between the prospective parties to the proposed arrangement, or

(b) that for any other reason arising out of the relative bargaining position of the prospective parties any of the terms of the proposed arrangement cannot be agreed,

that health service body may refer the terms of the proposed arrangement to the Secretary of State for determination under this section.

9) Where a reference is made to the Secretary of State under subsection (7) or (8), he may determine the matter himself or appoint a person to consider and determine it in accordance with regulations.

10) "The appropriate person" means the Secretary of State or the person appointed under subsection (9).

11) By the determination of a reference under subsection (8) the appropriate person may specify terms to be included in the proposed arrangement and may direct that it be proceeded with.

12) A determination of a reference under subsection (7) may contain such directions (including directions as to payment) as the appropriate person considers appropriate to resolve the matter in dispute.

13) The appropriate person may by the determination in relation to an NHS contract vary the terms of the arrangement or bring it to an end (but this does not affect the generality of the power of determination under subsection (7)).

14) Where an arrangement is so varied or brought to an end—

(a) subject to paragraph (b), the variation or termination must be treated as being effected by agreement between the parties, and

(b) the directions included in the determination by virtue of subsections (11) or (12) may contain such provisions as the appropriate person considers appropriate in order to give effect to the variation or to bring the arrangement to an end.

15) Payments made for the purposes of this Act by a commissioner to a provider may be designated as being a grant made by the commissioner to the provider for the purposes of the European Directive 2014/24/EU of the European Parliament and the Council.

16) Where a commissioner enters or proposes to enter into an NHS contract under this section the commissioner shall also be entitled to provide that the provider has an exclusive right to provide those services for a defined period which for each such designation shall not exceed 10 years.

17) Where a commissioner has made a designation under subsection (16) above it shall be entitled to remove the designation at any time.

18) Any person who is aggrieved at the award of a designation to a provider under subsection (16) above may refer the matter to the Secretary of State for determination under this section.

19) Notwithstanding the provisions of subsection (1) above, an arrangement between a commissioner and a provider for the provision of goods or services for the purpose of the health service shall not take effect as an NHS contract if, but only if—

(a) the terms of the arrangement are reduced to writing and have been signed by or on behalf of the commissioner and provider;

(b) the terms of the arrangement record in writing that—

      (i) the parties have each proposed that the arrangement shall not operate as an NHS contract; and

      (i) the arrangements will continue to remain in force between the parties regardless as to whether the Secretary of State makes a determination under subsection (20) below;

    (c) notice in writing of the arrangement has been given to the Secretary of State within 21 days of the date that the arrangement has been made together with a statement of the reasons why each of the commissioner and the provider wish the arrangement not to take effect as an NHS contract.

20) Where the Secretary of State is given notice under subsection (19) above the Secretary of State may determine that the arrangement shall take effect as an NHS contract.

21) Any determination by the Secretary of State under subsection (20) shall be made by the Secretary of State within 3 months of the date when the Secretary of State is given notice of the arrangement.'

PART 2

AMENDMENTS TO THE FINANCIAL POWERS OF NHS FOUNDATION TRUSTS AND NHS TRUSTS, AS AMENDED BY THE HEALTH AND SOCIAL CARE ACT 2012

7. Provision of goods and services by NHS foundation trusts

For section 43 of the National Health Service Act 2006 as amended by section 164 of the Health and Social Care Act 2012 substitute—

'43. Provision of goods and services and non-health service patient income cap

1) The principal purpose of an NHS foundation trust is the provision of goods and services for the purposes of the health service in England.

2) An NHS foundation trust may provide goods and services for any purposes related to—

    (a) the provision of services provided to individuals for or in connection with the prevention, diagnosis or treatment of illness, and

    (b) the promotion and protection of public health.

3) An NHS foundation trust shall ensure that its total income from the provision of goods and services for provision of services provided to individuals for or in connection with the prevention, diagnosis or treatment of illness otherwise than for the health services or for which charges are made by the trust is not greater than either—

    (a) such percentage of its total income from the provision of goods and services in connection with the prevention, diagnosis or treatment of illness as the Secretary of State shall direct; or

    (b) such higher percentage as shall be determined by the Secretary of State for an individual NHS foundation trust.

4) Every NHS foundation trust that undertakes the provision of goods and services to individuals for or in connection with the prevention, diagnosis or treatment of illness otherwise than for the health services or for which charges are made by the trust shall ensure that—

    (a) the provision of such goods and services do not have any adverse impact on the ability of the trust to carry on its principal purpose; and

(b) health service patients who are provided with services by the trust under this Act benefit from the trust's provision of such services.

5) The Secretary of State shall publish a statement of the principles that the Secretary of State will apply in considering applications by NHS foundation trusts under subsection (3) (b) above.

6) An NHS foundation trust may also carry on activities other than those mentioned in subsection (2) for the purpose of making additional income provided the NHS foundation trust is able to demonstrate to Monitor that—

(a) such activities ensure that it is better able to carry on its principal purpose; and

(b) that health service patients who are provided services by the trust benefit from such other activities of the NHS foundation trust.

7) Each annual report prepared by an NHS foundation trust must include an assessment of the impact that income received by the trust under sub-sections (3) and (6) has had on the provision by the trust of goods and services for the health service and how the provisions in this section have been satisfied by the trust.

8) The annual report of the NHS foundation trusts must include the views of the council of governors of the trust as to whether the provisions of this section have been satisfied where the trust has carried out any activities of a kind mentioned in subsection (3) and (6) above.

9) Each document prepared by an NHS foundation trust under

paragraph 27 of Schedule 7 (forward plan) must include information about—

(a) the activities other than the provision of goods and services for the purposes of the health service in England that the trust proposes to carry on,

(b) the income it expects to receive from doing so, and

(c) how the trust proposes to satisfy the conditions set out in this section in respect of each such activity.

10) Where a document which is being prepared under paragraph 27 of Schedule 7 contains a proposal that an NHS foundation trust carry on an activity of a kind mentioned in subsections (3) and (6), the council of governors of the trust must inform Monitor of its views on whether the conditions set out in this section will be satisfied in relation to the proposed activity.'

8. NHS income and provision of goods and services

After paragraph 14(4) of schedule 4 to the National Health Service Act 2006 add—

'4A) An NHS trust shall ensure that its total income from the provision of goods and services for provision of services provided to individuals for or in connection with the prevention, diagnosis or treatment of illness otherwise than for the health services or for which charges are made by the trust is not greater than either—

(a) such percentage of its total income from the provision of goods and services in connection with the prevention, diagnosis or treatment of illness as the Secretary of State shall direct;

(b) such higher percentage as shall be determined by the Secretary of State.

'4B) Every NHS trust that undertakes the provision of goods and services to individuals for or in connection with the prevention, diagnosis or treatment of illness otherwise than for the health services or for which charges are made by the trust shall ensure that—

(a) the provision of such goods and services do not have any adverse impact on the ability of the trust to carry on its principal purpose; and

(b) health service patients who are provided with services by the trust under this Act benefit from the trust's provision of such services.

4C) The Secretary of State shall publish a statement of the principles that the Secretary of State will apply in considering applications by NHS trusts under subsection (5)(b) above.'

PART 3

AMENDMENT OF PROVISIONS IN THE HEALTH AND SOCIAL CARE ACT 2012 RELATING TO COMPETITION AND PROCUREMENT IN THE HEALTH SERVICE AND CONNECTED AMENDMENTS

9. NHS trusts provision of non-health services

1) Notwithstanding the provisions in Part 3 of the Health and Social Care Act 2012, no legally enforceable procurement obligations shall be imposed on NHS commissioners in relation to any arrangement which is proposed to take effect or takes effect by way of an NHS contract.

2) Regulation 6 of the Public Contracts Regulations 2006 shall be amended by adding the following after Regulation 6(2)—

'2A) These Regulations do not apply to the seeking of offers for the supply of any services that are proposed to be included within an NHS contract.'

10. Repeals

Sections 62(2), 62(3), 62(10), 67(3)(a), and 72 to 80 of the Health and Social Care Act 2012 are repealed.

11. Exemptions from the Competition Act 1998

Notwithstanding the provisions in Part 3 of the Health and Social Care Act 2012—

a) The Competition Act 1998 shall not apply to the discharge of any functions by the Secretary of State or an NHS body in relation to the exercise of powers or the discharge of duties under the National Health Service Act 2006.

b) Any person commissioning or providing services for the purpose of the health service shall not for that purpose be an undertaking for the purposes of the Competition Act 1998.

c) The Enterprise Act 2002 shall not apply to any proposed merger involving an NHS or an NHS foundation trust.

12. Mergers of NHS trusts or foundation trusts to require the consent of the Secretary of State

Any merger involving an NHS Trust or an NHS Foundation Trust or the acquisition or disposal of significant property by an NHS Trust or an NHS Foundation Trust shall require the consent of the Secretary of State.

13. Regulations requiring NHS trust and foundation trust mergers to be in patients' interests

1) In discharge of the Secretary of State's duties under the National Health Act 2006, as amended by the Health and Social Care Act 2012, the Secretary of State may make Regulations which require the Secretary of State to provide approval in writing of—

   (a) any merger involving an NHS trust or an NHS foundation trust;

   (b) the acquisition or disposal of significant property by an NHS trust or an NHS foundation trust.

2) Regulations may provide that the Secretary of State should only give an approval under subsection (1) above if the Secretary of State is satisfied that the proposed merger or property acquisition or disposal is in the interests of patients.

3) The Secretary of State may provide guidance about—

   (a) the circumstances in which an acquisition or disposal of property by an NHS trust or an NHS foundation trust shall be significant;

   (b) the processes that an NHS trust or an NHS foundation trust should follow in order to seek the consent of the Secretary of State; and

   (c) how the Secretary of State will apply any patient interest test set out in Regulations.

PART 4
THE NHS AND NATIONAL OR INTERNATIONAL AGREEMENTS

14. NHS exemptions from proposed Transatlantic Trade and Investment Partnership Treaty

1) No ratification by a Minister of the Crown of the proposed Transatlantic Trade and Investment Partnership Treaty shall cause any legally enforceable procurement or competition obligations to be imposed on any NHS body entering into any arrangement for the provision of health services in any part of the health service.

2) In this section 'any part of the health service' shall mean any part of the health service in England under the National Health Service Act 2006, the health service in Scotland under the National Health Service (Scotland) Act 1978, the health service in Wales under the National Health Service (Wales) Act 2006 or the health service in Northern Ireland operated by the Department of Health, Social Services and Public Safety under the Northern Ireland Act 1998.

PART 5
GENERAL

15. Extent, citation and commencement

1) Sections 1 to 13 of this Act apply to England only.

2) Sections 14 and 15 of this Act apply to England, Wales, Scotland and Northern Ireland.

3) This Act may be cited as the National Health Service (Amended Duties and Powers) Act 2014.

4) This Act comes into force three months after it is passed.

Annex C

Response to the National Health Service (Amended Duties and Powers) Bill 2014, published on 7 November 2014 ('the Efford Bill')

Professor Allyson M. Pollock, Peter Roderick and David Price
Centre for Primary Care and Public Health, Queen Mary, University of London
11 November 2014 (corrected, 12 November 2014, see footnote 1)

Summary

The Efford Bill's proposed repeal of the 'Competition' sections of the 2012 Health and Social Care Act is (subject to one point of clarification) to be welcomed as a step in the right direction of reducing procurement and tendering procedures.

At the same time, however, the Bill accepts the 2012 Act's abolition of the Secretary of State's duty to provide – remarkably, given the long title of the Bill. It would replace it with a commissioning duty that would put in place a 100% commissioner–provider split and so extend the market structures that have been increasingly applied to the NHS over the last 25 years beyond the pre-2012 position.

The Bill gives rise to a number of points of concern. As well as not abolishing the commissioner–provider split, it would for example:

- appear to defer unnecessarily to EU competition law;
- leave untouched the power of clinical commissioning groups (CCGs) to arrange services they consider appropriate;
- not reverse the 2012 Act's prospective abolition of NHS trusts, and their transformation into NHS foundation trusts or take over by private companies; and
- leave Monitor in place with the same main duty, without a statutory purpose and continuing to licence private providers.

Further clarification is also required as regards the provisions covering the Transatlantic Trade and Investment Partnership Treaty, The National Health Service (Procurement, Patient Choice and Competition) (No. 2) Regulations 2013, and use of the term 'service of general economic interest'.

A Table in the Appendix below sets out our provisional views as to whether some of the key provisions in the Bill deserve to be supported or opposed and where clarification is needed.

1. Repeal of 'Competition' sections

The Bill proposes to repeal the 'Competition' sections of the 2012 Health and Social Care Act. Subject to one point of clarification, this is to be welcomed as a step in the right direction of reducing procurement and tendering procedures. This reduction would appear to be the result of Clause 10, which would repeal sections 72–80 of the 2012 Act, entitled 'Competition'.

This would, for example, remove the power to make regulations on procurement, patient choice and competition under section 75 – although the Bill does not expressly state that the current Regulations made under section 75 – The National Health Service (Procurement, Patient Choice and Competition) (No. 2) Regulations 2013 – would be revoked. This needs clarification.

2. More duties and powers to the Secretary of State

The Bill proposes to give more duties and powers over the NHS to the Secretary of State, compared with the position since the 2012 Health and Social Care Act.

These include:

- the duty to arrange provision of listed services (currently the duty of CCGs), with powers to delegate this duty to, and to direct, NHS England and CCGs (Clause 3);
- a general power to direct CCGs and NHS England (as well as NHS trusts and Special Health Authorities, as currently) (Clause 5);
- a power to direct that NHS foundation trusts and NHS trusts cannot raise more than an unspecified percentage of their income from (essentially) private patients – including the power to direct different percentages for different individual trusts (Clauses 7 and 8); and
- having to give consent to any merger involving an NHS trust of foundation trusts or to their acquisition or disposal of significant property (Clause 12).

3. Points of concern

The Bill gives rise to a number of points of concern:

1. It would not 're-establish the Secretary of State's legal duty to provide national health services in England', as stated in the long title of the Bill. This is because Clause 1 of the Bill repeats the 2012 Act's 'duty to exercise functions to secure provision' – rather than the 'duty

to provide or secure provision' in place from 1946–2012; and because Clause 3 is a 'duty to arrange provision' rather than a 'duty to provide' as it was until the 2012 Act[133] – and Clause 3 also drops the long-standing requirement to do so 'throughout England'.

2. The Bill imposes a duty on the Secretary of State to 'ensure that the health service is a public service which delivers services of a general economic interest and operates on the basis of social solidarity' (Clause 1(2)(b)).

The concept of 'services of general economic interest' derives from Articles 14 and 106(2) of the Treaty on the Functioning of the European Union and Protocol No 26 of that Treaty. The European Commission and Member States share competence for these services insofar as Member States may seek derogations from EU competition rules subject to the agreement of the Commission. Agreement must be sought on a case-by-case basis. By contrast, the Commission has no authority over services of general non-economic interest, which are entirely the responsibility of member states. The terms are not defined and citing several court cases[134] the European Commission has said that Member States 'have considerable discretion when it comes to defining what they regard as services of general economic interest'.[135]

It has not been determined whether the NHS is a service of general economic activity. For example, in 2003 the Spanish Health Service

---

133 This is a correction. The original version of this response read 'until the 1946 Act'.

134 Case T-17/02 *Fred Olsen* [2005] ECR II-2031, paragraph 216; Case T-289/03 *BUPA and Others* v *Commission* [2008] ECR II-81, paragraphs 166–169; Case T-309/04 *TV2* [2008] ECR II-2935, paragraphs 113 *et seq*.

135 *Guide to the application of the European Union rules on state aid, public procurement and the internal market to services of general economic interest, and in particular to social services of general interest*, Brussels, 29.4.2013 SWD(2013) 53 final/2, Commission Staff Working Document, available here: http://ec.europa.eu/competition/state_aid/overview/new_guide_eu_rules_procurement_en.pdf.

was held by the European Court of Justice not to be such a service.[136] It is at least strongly arguable that the NHS is also not such a service.

Last year the Commission stated that '[t]he organisation of public hospitals which are an integral part of a national health service and are almost entirely based on the principle of solidarity, funded directly from social security contributions and other State resources, and which provide their services free of charge to affiliated persons on the basis of universal coverage' are an example of 'non-economic activities of a purely social nature'.[137]

The Bill therefore appears to defer to EU competition law unnecessarily by imposing this duty on the Secretary of State.

3. The Bill would render the NHS a 100% commissioner/provider service. This was not the position before the 2012 Act, and so in this respect the Bill would extend the market in the NHS beyond its previous position under Labour governments – for example, Primary Care Trusts were both providers and commissioners. Yet commissioning remains an unproven policy. In 2010 the Health Select Committee damned commissioning as '20 years of costly failure'.[138]

4. The Bill leaves in place the wide power of CCGs to commission health services they consider appropriate under section 3A of the NHS Act 2006, inserted in 2012. This power allows CCGs to operate outside the Secretary of State's duty proposed in Clause 3 (which only replaces section 3 of the 2006 Act). The power in Clause 5 to direct CCGs about the exercise of their duties and powers could be used to limit the operation of section 3A, but whether and the extent to which this would happen in practice would depend on the particular

---

136 Case T-319/99 FENIN [2003] ECR II-357.

137 See note 2, at page 33.

138 http://www.parliament.uk/business/news/2010/03/20-years-of-costly-failure-mps-verdict-on-nhs-commissioning/

government, and it could not be used to take the power away.

5. The Bill would not reverse the 2012 Act's prospective abolition of NHS trusts, and their transformation into NHS foundation trusts or take over by private companies. The 2012 Act requires all NHS trusts to become NHS foundation trusts, and if they cannot they will be merged, closed or taken over by private companies. This would remain the position.

6. The Bill would leave Monitor in place with the same main duty, without a statutory purpose and continuing to licence private providers.

4. A number of the provisions also require clarification

1. The Transatlantic Trade and Investment Partnership Treaty

Clause 14 provides that ratification of the Transatlantic Trade and Investment Partnership Treaty shall not cause any legally enforceable procurement or competition obligations to be imposed on any NHS body entering into any arrangement for the provision of health services, in England, Scotland, Wales and Northern Ireland.

This raises a number of questions:

i) Ratification of a treaty follows signature. It is a step required for a treaty to become binding in international law. Once ratification has occurred therefore, the obligations referred to would become binding in international law. So Clause 14 appears to purport to set up a conflict between the UK's international obligations and domestic law. We are not convinced that this formulation would have that effect and clarification is needed as to whether Clause 14 would be effective.

ii) The heading of Clause 14 is 'NHS exemptions from proposed [TTIP]'. However, the text of the Clause does not exempt the NHS. Rather, its terms are limited to 'procurement or competition obligations to be imposed on any NHS body entering into any arrangement for the provision of health services'. It should therefore be clarified whether it would extend to obligations of the UK (as opposed to obligations of any NHS body), whether it would apply to both commissioners and providers, and the definition of NHS body should be made clear. It should also be explained why it would not extend to other obligations, such as (for example) the ousting of the jurisdiction of the UK courts, or to the rights of private companies to bid for contracts.

2. The National Health Service (Procurement, Patient Choice and Competition) (No. 2) Regulations 2013

These Regulations were made under section 75, of the 2012 Act, which would be repealed. They require commissioners (for example) to advertise new NHS contracts unless the services are only capable of being provided by a single provider. The Bill does not provide that these Regulations would be revoked, although its repeal of section 75 would mean that no future regulations of this type could be made. It might be implied that the Regulations would be revoked, but this should be clarified.

3. 'Service of general economic interest'

In view of the apparently unnecessary engagement of EU competence by characterising the NHS as a service of general economic interest – and considering other provisions in the Bill which appear to point in the opposite direction (e.g., the service being operated on basis of social solidarity (Clause 1(2)((b), and commissioners and providers not being 'undertakings' for the purposes of the Competition Act 1998 (Clause 11(b)) – it would be helpful for an explanation to be provided for use of the term in Clause 1(2)(b).

5. Conclusion

The Bill's proposed repeal of the 'Competition' sections of the 2012 Health and Social Care Act is (subject to one point of clarification) to be welcomed as a step in the right direction of reducing procurement and tendering procedures.

At the same time, however, the Bill accepts the 2012 Act's abolition of the Secretary of State's duty to provide – remarkably, given the long title of the Bill. It would replace it with a commissioning duty that would put in place a 100% commissioner–provider split and so extend the market structures that have been increasingly applied to the NHS over the last 25 years beyond the pre-2012 position.

Appendix

There is little chance of the Efford Bill becoming law.

Procedurally, we support it going forward, as this will allow for more thorough debate, and for tabling significant amendments in line with the NHS Reinstatement Bill.

Substantively, we have welcomed its repeal of the 'Competition' sections of the 2012 Health and Social Care Act as a step in the right direction of reducing procurement and tendering procedures – subject to clarification that the National Health Service (Procurement, Patient Choice and Competition) (No. 2) Regulations 2013 would also be revoked.

These are the Regulations that require commissioners to advertise new NHS contracts unless the services are only capable of being provided by a single provider. We have asked Mr Efford for clarification on this but he has not (yet) answered our email.

Our position on other key aspects has been set out in the Table below:

Clause	Response
1 (Duty on the Secretary of State to promote comprehensive health service), substituting a new section for s.1 of the NHS Act 2006	Oppose new s.1(1) and new s.1(2)(a), and replace with 1946–2012 wording Clarification sought of new s.1(2)(b) Support new s.1(2)(c) Oppose new s.1(3) (2012 insertion) Support new s.1(4) (long-standing provision)
2 (Exercise of the Secretary of State's powers), inserting a new section as s.2C of the NHS Act 2006 (Duties and guidance in respect of cooperation and social solidarity)	Support
3 (Duty on the Secretary of State regarding provision of certain services), substituting a new section 3 of the NHS Act 2006	Oppose new s.3(1), and replace with duty to provide throughout England
5 (Power of Secretary of State to direct certain health service bodies), substituting a new s.8 of the NHS Act 2006	Support and extend
10 (Repeals)	Support, but clarification sought regarding the National Health Service (Procurement, Patient Choice and Competition) (No. 2) Regulations 2013
11 (Exemptions from the Competition Act 1998)	Support
14 (NHS exemptions from proposed Transatlantic Trade and Investment Partnership Treaty)	Clarification sought

Annex D

English translation of the full German Constitutional Court's ruling, paras 395–7

395. In 1997, the Social Agreement, which, due to a lack of political consensus, had first come into being as an independent instrument under international law beside the Treaty of Maastricht, was incorporated into Community law. Article 136 to Article 150 ECT [Treaty Establishing the European Community] contain competences *inter alia* in the areas of social security, basic and advanced vocational training, codecision, dialogue with the social partners and working conditions (see on the details for instance Kingreen, *Das Sozialstaatsprinzip im europäischen Verfassungsverbund*, 2003, pp. 295 et seq.). These provisions are complemented by Article 13 ECT, which is the legal basis of the non-discrimination directives, Article 39 ECT, which provides for the freedom of movement for workers, and by the social fundamental rights laid down in the Charter of Fundamental Rights, which devotes its entire Title IV to them under the heading of 'Solidarity' (Article 27 to Article 38 of the Charter). The Court of Justice of the European Communities, in particular, has for some years now interpreted citizenship of the Union as the nucleus of European solidarity and has

further developed it in its case law based on Article 18 in conjunction with Article 12 ECT. This line of case law represents the attempt to found a European social identity by promoting participation of the citizens of the Union in the respective social systems of the Member States (see the contributions in Hatje/Huber, *Unionsbürgerschaft und soziale Rechte*, 2007, and Kadelbach, *Unionsbürgerrechte*, in: Ehlers, *Europäische Grundrechte und Grundfreiheiten*, 2nd ed. 2005, pp. 553 et seq.; Hailbronner, *Unionsbürgerschaft und Zugang zu den Sozialsystemen*, JZ 2005, pp. 1138 et seq.).

396. The Treaty of Lisbon follows this line of development. In its second recital, the Preamble of the Treaty on the Functioning of the European Union states it is resolved 'to ensure the economic and social progress' of the Member States 'by common action'. The objectives of the Treaty on European Union are adapted in such a way that the Union aims at a 'highly competitive social market economy, aiming at full employment and social progress' (Article 3.3(1) Lisbon TEU [Treaty of the European Union]). At the same time, the aim of 'free and undistorted competition' is deleted from the operative part of the Treaty on European Union and is shifted to Protocol no. 27 on the Internal Market and on Competition. A new cross-sectional clause (Article 9 TFEU) is intended to ensure that requirements linked to the promotion of a high level of employment, the guarantee of adequate social protection, the fight against social exclusion and a high level of education is taken into account in all policies and activities of the Union (other new elements in the social area are introduced by the Treaty of Lisbon through Article 5.3 <coordination of the Member States' social policies>, Article 21.3 <citizenship of the Union and social security>, Article 152 <role of the social partners> and Article 165.2 TFEU <social function of sport>; Protocol no. 29 mentions the connection of the existence of

a system of public broadcasting with the social needs of each society). 397. Political initiatives and programmes which supplement the law and lend it concrete shape correspond to the legal framework of action. In its Presidency conclusions, the Brussels European Council of 11 and 12 December 2007 explicitly recognised that the subjects social progress and the protection of workers' rights, public services as an indispensable instrument of social and regional cohesion, the responsibility of Member States for the delivery of education and health services, the essential role and wide discretion of national, regional and local Governments in providing, commissioning and organising non-economic services of general interest Union are of high importance (Bulletin EU 12-2008, I-17 (Annex 1)).

Annex E

Charter 2010

The UK is in the midst of a deep financial and economic crisis. We also face a General Election no later than June 2010. The nature of the crisis is profound.

At the same time public disillusionment with MPs and politics has never been higher. Trust in the working of the banking and financial system has never been lower. The UK fiscal deficit – the difference between income and spending – stands near to £180 billion, or about 13 per cent of GDP. This deficit has not just been induced by the global recession. It is in part the result of national economic decisions. The UK deficit is the worst among the top industrial economies of the G20 group, which includes Japan and the US. It is the worst deficit Britain has had since the Second World War. It can be dealt with successfully if handled intelligently and with courage and consistency. Predictably, the party political battle ahead promises to be fierce. Labour will fight to stay in government, the Conservatives to become the government and the Liberal Democrats to be part of the government. Yet when the electoral conflict is over, no one party may have sufficient MPs to govern on its own and the country will face a 'hung' parliament and the considerable risks in having, within months, another election. There are immense political and economic dangers ahead if we fail to plan now on how to transform a hung parliament into a representative and democratic government. With confidence in the UK economy at a low ebb, the international financial community will need the assurance of a coherent, credible and lasting government to emerge out of a hung parliament.

Charter 2010 is for now, it is about post-electoral planning in the event of a hung parliament in 2010. It asks the country to think before the election about what would be in the best interests of Britain if there was to be a hung parliament. It is an attempt to prise open the closed world of conventional politics and let fresh air into it. Some politicians already portray any democratic result in 2010 that deprives their party of a large majority in Parliament as leading to weak or indecisive government. Yet a government supported by more than one political party in 2010 could gain in strength from having a larger democratic base. We have experienced government representing only 36 per cent of voters since 2005. In 2010 a government will have to persuade voters of the need for painful measures to revive our economy. A government made up of more than one party would almost certainly represent more than 50 per cent of voters and would be better able to tap into the British people's innate commonsense and readiness to make sacrifices in the national interest.

Charter 2010 believes that all voters, when considering which candidate to support in their constituency, have the right to know not just how the party leaders but how the individual candidates would respond to a hung parliament. This is particularly so if party leaders have chosen not to indicate in advance that because of policy differences they would prefer to negotiate with a particular party. Voters have the right to know how their candidate would work within an overall result that produces a hung parliament. If elected as an MP, they may not be prepared for their party to negotiate with a particular party – in which case they should be prepared to reveal that – or they may believe their party should try to govern as a minority government, with the aim of securing a majority at an early second election. Alternatively, they may accept the legitimacy of negotiating in the first instance in a way which takes into account votes cast by the electorate as a whole. Whatever their view, they should be prepared to argue its merits.

As the election draws nearer, these are not theoretical issues to be avoided but legitimate questions that need to be answered in the democratic debate which should accompany General Elections.

The Two Principles of Charter 2010

Charter 2010 is designed to help individual voters in their constituencies to debate how any hung parliament can be transformed into a strong, representative majority government. It aims to persuade potential MPs and the leaders of the political parties to pledge to act after the 2010 election in accordance with two principles:

1) The electors are entitled to ask that party leaders and candidates are straight with them about a hung parliament before they cast their votes.

   - If they make an arrangement with another party prior to the election, they should say so.
   - If there is a party they would not wish their party to collaborate with in government, again they should say so.
   - If they are open-minded about the arrangements that might be made after an election which did not produce a sustainable majority for any one party, they should commit to take proper account of the electors' wishes (as expressed both in terms of the

number of votes cast as well as the number of MPs elected) when considering with which party or parties their party should first negotiate to produce a stable and representative government.

2) All the candidates and party leaders should be asked to agree that the principal objective of forming a multi-party supported government for a four-year fixed term following an indecisive election result would be to enable such a government to focus on dealing with the economic crisis – undistracted by short-term electoral, parliamentary and party political considerations. Thus all the participating political parties would undertake not to precipitate a further General Election until at least the fourth anniversary of the 2010 election; and the Prime Minister of the government so formed would agree not to seek a dissolution before that date, other than with the support of all the political parties supporting that government.